Grandpa's Store

Grandpa's Store

Glenn Mollette

Johnny House Press
Newburgh, Indiana

In Memory:
Melissa Bowen - Mama Mollette
John C. and Ina Ward Hinkle –
Grandpa and Mama Hinkle
Walter and Eula Hinkle Mollette –
Dad and Mom

For:
Geneva, Wanda, Arvel and Clyde

For Carole
Thanks for everything! Thank you
for your love and support.
Your interest and commitment to
this project has truly been a work
of devotion. Thank you for reading,
reading, editing and editing!

Table of Contents

Introduction

Grandpa's Store is a reflection of my childhood days. The era is between about 1958 – 1971. The story ends at the death of my Grandmother Ina Hinkle.

This story is based on what I saw, heard and experienced as a child and young teenager.

There is so much most of us do not know about our family's past. When we are young we are too busy to talk to the old folks. When we finally have time to care they are gone.

This book is filled with stories from a wonderful time in my life. I didn't write everything so there is more for another book. These stories are based on actual events as I remember them. In certain cases, incidents, characters and timelines have been changed for dramatic purposes. Certain characters may be composites, or entirely fictitious. Any name that sounds recognizable is merely a coincidence.

Chapter 1
Earliest Memory

Riding in a baby carriage is the way to travel when you're two years old. Unfortunately our driveway was gravel. Our little baby carriage didn't have shocks and that was a bumpy ride! It could have been Geneva or Wanda pushing that carriage. For the life of me I can't recall. I do remember it was one of those beautiful mountain days. There were sunny skies and clean air, as best I remember.

I remember sitting in a high chair at Uncle Junior and Aunt Lucille Hinkle's house. Lucille was feeding me Twinkies. She may have been babysitting me. I was strapped into that chair and I remember waving my hands and grunting for another bite of Twinkie. Lucille always had a smile and was a nice babysitter.

Mom gave birth to me when she was 38. Two sisters and two brothers were already in the household. Geneva was 14 at my birth, Wanda 13, Arvel 12 and Clyde almost 10. Needless to say I was a surprise child, an unplanned pregnancy. With four other kids in the house I was not exactly a needed presence. With all the inconvenience of a new baby at the age of 38, Mom and Dad kept me for better or for worse.

All 11 pounds of me came into the world on January 10, 1955. Born in the Paintsville, Kentucky hospital, the delivering doctor presented me to my mother as "Big George."

My brothers and sisters were much older than I. My dad was a busy coalmining father. My mother kept a house going for a family of seven. Somebody had to take care of the baby.

We had a coal burning stove in our house for a number of years. This stove sat in Mom and Dad's bedroom. I slept in a baby bed that was in the corner of this bedroom when I wasn't in my mom and dad's bed.

One Sunday morning we had a big fire going in that coal burning stove and I climbed up into my dad's lap. It seemed like I was there the entire morning. We were in an old cushioned rocking chair. I think I even snoozed a bit while the warmth of that stove permeated the house. I was probably only there for an hour or so. Uncle Seburn, from just up the road and up the holler, came by for one of his usual visits. He sat for an hour or two smoking a few cigarettes. My mother always kept an ashtray for him and other family members who came by the house to visit and smoke.

Sleeping in the baby bed was like being in jail – sort of. There were bars on that bed and early on it was a difficult place to escape from. I was in that baby bed one day when my dad was preparing to drive a truck to Ohio to buy a load of hay. Mom and Dad stood there by the baby bed and had a passionate hug and a kiss. What's a baby supposed to do when his mom and dad are all wrapped up in each other hugging and kissing? After their embrace Dad was off to buy hay for his cattle.

One of my more dramatic nights in that baby bed was Christmas Eve. I was anxious for Santa Claus to come. I had been looking at the JC Penney's catalog since September and had a wish list a mile long for Christmas. Of course I already understood that Santa Claus could only bring a couple of gifts because he had a lot of boys and girls to buy for around the world. That was okay with me. Just the idea of the jolly big guy coming to see me was exciting. So, I was all wrapped up in my baby bed in anticipation of the big evening. I might see Santa. After all, the coal stove was right in our bedroom and Santa came down chimneys. This was the only chimney we had, so I guessed this was how he would be making his entrance.

But wait. Something bad was happening. My dad was putting wood and coal in the stove. The fire in the stove roared and I began to cry. This irritated my dad. He didn't understand why on earth I was crying. "How is Santa Claus going to get in the house with all of that fire in the stove?" "I'll unlock the front door," responded Mom quickly. "Santa Claus uses front doors many times because not everybody has a chimney." I was so relieved. At least now Santa could make his visit.

The coal stove was a key source of our heat during my early childhood years. Eventually Dad would have a furnace installed but for awhile we had a couple of natural gas stoves and the coal stove that got us through the winter.

One January morning I woke up and had wet the bed. It was cold in the house and Mom and Dad were rebuilding the fire. By the time I got out of the bed the stove was putting out some nice heat and was red-hot. I stripped off my underwear because I was wet and cold and ran naked as a jaybird over to the stove and placed my bottom as close as I could to that stove – too close. My bottom went right up against the searing hot coal stove. I yelped as I severely scorched my bottom.

For the next two weeks it was very hard to sit anywhere. My mother was constantly putting some kind of ointment or salve on my bottom. Even worse, when we were visiting at Mama's, she had to pull down my pants and show Mama and her sister

Kathleen my bottom. It wasn't very pretty at that time.

Chapter 2
Mama Mollette

Dad's mom had lived with us since my earliest memory. I don't remember when she moved in. I just remember that she was in our house. For a little three to four-year-old child she was a hoot to have in the house. She entertained and babysat and was always looking for a way to pacify me. It seemed that she always kept peppermint candy in the trunk in her bedroom. She probably didn't, but I can clearly remember a couple of occasions when Mama was going to her trunk to find a juicy peppermint piece for me.

Mama fit the classic description of a grandma. She looked like a grandma and acted like a grandma but was always dressed nicely and often had on her jewelry. She didn't move around too quickly. She was probably at least 40 pounds overweight. At the age of 80 her vision had dimmed. No one knows if Mama had cataracts, glaucoma, or some type of macular degeneration. Medical care in Martin County was not exactly state of the art in 1958. We had one family doctor for the entire county. His name was Doc Ford.

Mama did have a sense of humor and was a storyteller. I never wanted my Mommy to leave me when I was a child. If she wasn't in the house I wanted to know where she was. Mama was always on the lookout for how she might entertain me if my mother had to leave the house or go somewhere. She had a little trick that always won me over. As soon as Mom left the house we would start looking for Santa Claus. If he came around "We'll catch him and tie him up and take all his presents," she said with a convincing twinkle. I always bought it. Santa never showed up but Mama had a story like that or something similar to keep my attention while my mother was out of the house. Some things are instilled in us as children. Some of my creative imagination surely came from Mama Mollette.

Recently, I was told that Mama could play a fiddle and also play the guitar. I never heard or saw her doing either which means she must have given up playing in her older years. We did have a fiddle in our house. It was upstairs in a case for many years. I don't remember anybody ever playing that fiddle very well. However, it was probably the one that Mama had played. There has never been a time that I have not loved music and enjoyed thumping on a guitar. So much is passed along to us.

As a small child I always felt love from Mama Mollette. In my mind she was my mama. Across the creek and just slightly down the road was Grandpa and Grandma Hinkle's country store. That's where Grandpa and Ina worked. They were my mom's parents but I had a hard time calling Ina either mama or grandma. She was Ina. In my mind I could only have one mama and that was my dad's mother who slept in our house. Ina had a bit of a problem with me calling her Ina. On several occasions she asked "Can't you call me Grandma or Mama Hinkle?" "Yes, Ina," I would say.

Hurry Mommy, Mama is Dying!

Something went really wrong on December 8, 1958. Mama was feeling terribly bad. She was in her bed and she had not been out of bed much the last couple of days. Mom was worried about her and Ina and my aunt Maude were in the room. We didn't have a telephone. No one on the road where we lived had a telephone. However, Ina and Aunt Maude who lived about a half mile south of us were sitting in the room trying to talk to Mama. Her chest was hurting and so was at least one of her arms. Mom, Ina and Maude were taking turns rubbing her arms trying to alleviate the pain.

There was no phone to call an ambulance. We didn't even have access to a car. We owned a car but it was Dad's turn to carpool to the coal mine where he worked. His rider's car was parked in front of our house. Mom frantically ran out to the car to see if he had left keys in the car. It was locked and there was no sign of a key. I know in her desperation Mom hoped she could put Mama in that car and take her to see Doc Ford or to the Paintsville, Kentucky hospital which was a 30 minute mountain drive. She came back into the house to attend to Mama.

The pain grew worse and Mama lost control of her bladder. Mom went upstairs for fresh bed linens. Suddenly Ina and Maude, in almost unison said "Eula, come back, she's dying!" Running to the foot of the steps I began to repeat what I had just heard "Hurry Mommy, Mama is dying! Mommy, Mommy, Mama is dying!" Mom was on her way down the steps and took her place beside Mama's bed. I stood at the foot of the bed as the three of them held onto Mama. Mama struggled some and soon she was exhaling her last breath of air. The room was filled with tears that day. Mommy cried, Ina and Maude cried and I cried. That sweet, funny lady was now gone. The sorrow of her death and her absence overwhelmed our house.

Mama's body remained in the bed for most of the afternoon.

Dad was away in the mines but he returned about 5:00 that afternoon. Suddenly everything seemed to happen at once. My mother was giving instructions to one of my brothers to go to the store across the road and pick up some bread and cans of soup and a couple of other items. Daddy was now in the back bedroom standing over Mama's body. He bent down and put his arms around her and hugged her. Tears filled his eyes as he removed his arms. Within the hour the undertaker showed up. Someone must have driven to Inez to tell them. The funeral home people placed Mama on a gurney and took her out of the house. "Mommy where are they taking Mama?" I asked.

Within two days Mama was back in the house. This time she was stationed in her casket in the front bedroom. Our house on Stidham Road was relatively small. The flow of people didn't stop during the two days she lay in state.

There were at least 48 hours of nonstop activity once Mama's body was brought back. We had to sleep when we could. In those days it was normal for family and friends to stay up with the body the entire night or nights.

The funeral was also held in our house. People sang and the preacher preached from the bedroom. People were scattered everywhere throughout the house, on the front porch and around the outside of the house. When it was all over Mama was buried on the Hall Branch beside her husband Lafayette who was commonly called Lafe.

For at least two days our house was a place of nonstop activity. People were everywhere and there was food to eat. We only had one bathroom. I don't remember hearing that anything was stolen from the house. I don't remember hearing about any problems. People had gathered to share in the grief of losing Mama. Looking back at it, through the eyes of a child, the small county community spirit of love and support during our time of family grief was overwhelming.

Chapter 3
Ina Becomes Mama

A couple of days after Mama Mollette's funeral I walked across the creek and down the road to visit Ina and Grandpa Hinkle. My mother was extremely hesitant about me walking over there by myself. After all I was just getting ready to turn four.

Ina and Grandpa Hinkle ran the local grocery store and post office for Stidham. Grandpa was the official postmaster and the post office took up a small corner of the grocery store. Grocery items filled the rest of the shelves. I remember a soda pop cooler, a meat refrigerator and one freezer. The refrigerator was usually filled with a variety of meats. Bologna was a big item. My mother would sometimes buy a pound of bologna. Grandpa would take a big roll of bologna out of the refrigerator and slice off what he thought was close to a pound to weigh on the scale. Also in the refrigerator would be hamburger, wieners, pickle loaf and other meats.

The second cooler contained ice-cold soda pop. During the hot summer months when school was not in session I would get a cold pop out of that cooler. The soda sat down in a bit of icy water. The soda never turned icy but was cold enough to where it always felt like it was on the verge of turning to ice. When the temperature was 90 degrees there was nothing like a cold pop from Grandpa and Ina's store.

There was also a freezer for the ice cream. The best ice cream in the world was in that freezer. Fudge bars, sherbet push-ups, chocolate covered vanilla bars, ice cream sandwiches and more.

For a child of about four or five years old, putting my hands in the ice cream freezer was like reaching into a treasure chest.

Grandpa and Ina had an assortment of other items to sell. They sold feed for cattle as well as salt blocks that some cattle owners bought. Sometimes he had buckets and washtubs that people used to catch rainwater for washing clothes.

Out front sat two gasoline pumps. It was the closest place within several miles for people to buy gasoline. Some people pumped their gas themselves. Often Grandpa would pump it for them.

A car would pull up to the pumps with the customer remaining inside the car and Grandpa would open the door to the store and ask, "Would you like for me to draw your gas?" The customer would respond with "yel" and periodically there would be a "yes sir." Grandpa would go out to the pumps in his dress pants and dress shirt. I never saw him in denim or blue jeans of any kind. He would draw the gasoline and then collect $2.00. You could buy about 12 or more gallons of gasoline in that era for $2.00 so it was a common purchase.

Ina and Grandpa worked from early morning to the early evening in their store. Ina was often in the house cooking. She fixed breakfast, lunch and supper. In between meals she helped Grandpa in the store.

Beside the store was their two bedroom, one bath house. At the back of the store was another bathroom. Upstairs over the store there was a long attic type room that contained three beds. I remember Grandpa and Ina sleeping up over the store a lot. Several times I slept in one of those three beds.

"Glenn," said Ina "Mama Mollette is gone. You can now call

me Mama." Looking at her for what seemed a long five seconds I nodded my head and said, "Okay, Mama." And from then on it was Mama. Mama Hinkle.

Chapter 4
Working Hard in the Grocery Business

Mama and Grandpa started their first grocery just outside of a big white house they owned further up on south Milo Road. The store was small and the location was difficult to get to. I am told that you had to literally walk a long gravel lane, cross a small bridge across the creek and then drive a little further to get to the store.

Moving the store across the creek and about a half mile north would be a much better location. It would be a convenient stop on Stidham Road for shoppers, gasoline buyers and post office business.

The new store was a place of business and activity. I don't mean Wal-Mart activity. This was out in the middle of Appalachia. This was a day when there were many gravel roads and long winding mountain roads that everybody drove to get anywhere in East Kentucky. People said it used to take six or seven hours to drive to Lexington, Kentucky. I wouldn't know. My first trip to Lexington was when I was about 17 years old and was on the newly constructed Mountain Parkway. This was a super nice highway for 1972.

Our area of Stidham was isolated. It was a winding four-mile drive to Inez. Once we drove off Stidham Road then we would drive on Route 40. The rest of the way to Inez was paved and felt like an expressway during our day.

There was a grocery in Inez and the Fannin's had a grocery about three miles north just off the Fannin Bridge at the end of north Milo. There was a small post office on that end of the road giving that area the name of Milo. Fred Mills had a grocery store in Tomahawk next to the Tomahawk elementary school and Marcus Wells was growing a nice grocery store in the Tomahawk area.

Grandpa had the gasoline and grocery business for about a two-mile radius plus the gasoline business for those who passed by.

It seemed as if there was always somebody in the store buying something or someone buying gasoline. Sometimes Grandpa would get covered up with customer activity. He would stand at the counter with his pencil and paper. People would buy several items and bring them to the counter. Grandpa would then add up the purchases, figure the sales tax and bag up the grocery items.

He would go over his notes to make sure that what he was charging them was correct. This was a painstaking process especially when there were two or three other customers in the store wanting to buy something at the same time. Because they lived next door, Mama was always easily available when several cars pulled into the small parking area in front of the store. She would scurry out and try to assist other customers so they could keep the flow of business moving. This was not an everyday scene of business but I remember it happening several times.

The store business and overall life in general was a team effort by Grandma and Grandpa. They raised 10 children. They had nine of their own and their grandson James. James was the son of their youngest daughter Eva Nell.

My mother Eula was their fourth child. There were Haskel, Graden, John C., Jr. and then my mother Eula. After Eula there were Lorenz, Sebern, Kathleen, Eva Nell and Clyde. All of these were grown and had families by the time I came on the scene. I only remember James being with Mama and Grandpa and I remember him helping out in the store, as Grandpa needed him.

The model of Grandpa and Mama working side by side was a great model for a young child. It was a team effort of success. They were never rich. They probably never had a whole lot in a savings account. James once said, "Grandpa had $3,600 stashed behind his cigarette stand in the store. And that's all the money he really had when he died." This was money that James had paid him every month for a green Ford Galaxy 500. Grandpa had put the monthly $300 payment behind his cigarette stand according to James.

However, they took care of themselves. They worked. They worked long hours. They worked Saturdays. I don't know of a time they ever took a vacation. It was not a perfect world by any means but they did feed themselves, pay their own doctor bills, and save their money so they could pay cash for their cars, appliances and anything else they needed.

Grandpa and Mama were models of what two people can do when they work together. We've lost some of this in much of America today. Single parents try to survive as they raise one or more children. Massive numbers of couples go through one, two or more divorces. There is less and less stability and fewer long-term marriage partnerships. Every time a marriage dissolves there is a serious blow to the stability of both partners. There is financial loss. Most of the time in average America everybody loses something in a divorce whether it is cash, a house, a car, land, etc. This takes years to recover from, if recovery ever happens. One of the marriage partners always shoulders more of the parental responsibility than the other but both suffer, as do the children. This makes life more difficult as one now has to juggle kids, work, money and life in general. Two people who work in partnership have a better chance of overcoming general life obstacles if they work as a team.

Of course there is nothing worse than a marriage that never works together as a team. That's one reason so many marriages end in disaster. If two people constantly work against each other and separate of the other this only creates misery and an eventual demise of the marriage.

Two people working together as a team can go somewhere. They can earn enough money to live on, pay the bills, raise the kids and accomplish some of their passions in life.

I really don't know what Grandpa's passion was. I think he enjoyed owning his own business and determining his hours of work. He liked deciding his own paycheck and being his own boss. In the mix of all of this he and Mama were raising and providing for 10 children until they could become self-sustaining adults. Mama and Grandpa obviously bought into this together and they pulled it off.

This was early 1960 and Grandma and Grandpa Hinkle were in their early seventies.

Chapter 5
The Wandering Stranger

Before he owned a car Grandpa would take his wagon over to Inez to pick up supplies. He would have to go over Inez Hill. He once told a story about one interesting evening.

Grandpa had a couple of horses pulling his wagon. It was a simple quiet ride along the mountain road. As he started up the hill the horses seemed to be anxious. Suddenly a man appeared out of nowhere. He climbed on the back of Grandpa's wagon and began to ride up the hill.

"Well hello there sir. Looks like you are needing a ride up the hill." Grandpa said with a bit of irritation and anxiety. The man looked at Grandpa and said nothing. Grandpa shook the reins for the horses to go a little faster. This did not require much of a beckon as the horses where already giddy. The hill was steep and there was no way the horses could break into a full gallop.

Grandpa looked over his shoulder and the man was staring at him but did not smile and made no indication that he wanted to talk. "Sir, I don't mind giving you a ride but could you please tell me your name?" The man barely nodded his head but did not look away or flinch a muscle of any kind.

Grandpa was getting more nervous and did not know what to expect next or what kind of person he had on the back of his wagon. Possibly, the man was simply someone needing a ride to town. Maybe this man had a physical impairment and could not hear or speak. Or, maybe this was something else.

The horses trudged along up the hill and Grandpa was hardly

able to control the reins as the horses were becoming jumpy. Grandpa next felt some movement on the wagon and turned to see that the man had moved up closer to him. It was now almost pitch dark and he was having trouble seeing the man's face but he looked familiar.

Finally the horses arrived at the top of the mountain and were obviously tired from the climb but Grandpa feared stopping because he did not know what to expect next. Suddenly the man got off the wagon and began to walk toward the woods and disappeared. Grandpa moved along and planned to rest the horses a bit at the bottom of the hill. When he got to the bottom of the hill he was shaking from the unexplainable incident that had occurred.

Grandpa said he pondered about that man and what had taken place for a long time but eventually forgot about it. Years later, Grandpa was finally able to buy a car. He recalled that he was coming back from Inez when he saw someone by the side of the road hitchhiking. This was back in the day when we thought it was safer to pick up hitchhikers in the county. Pulling up beside the hitchhiker, Grandpa leaned over and opened the door of the car. The hitchhiker began to cry out "Oh no! Oh no! It's you!" The strange man slammed the door to Grandpa's car and ran off over the hill.

Grandpa hit the gas pedal and accelerated down the hill. Turning to drive up Stidham he suddenly realized this was the same man who had gotten on the back of his wagon years ago. Never again was he able to drive across the Inez Hill without looking for this wandering stranger.

The White Haired Man

Grandpa used to tell about a man who quit riding his horse over Inez Hill. Late one evening the man was riding his horse, Ol' Bill, up the hill. As he rode along a strange looking man jumped up and onto the back of his horse and threw his arms around him. The rider tried to shake the stranger off the horse but the stranger wouldn't budge. The horse took off up the Inez Hill and traveled faster than ever before.

The rider of the horse was becoming hysterical as he tried to dismount and flee for his life but the strange rider would not let him go. Finally when they got to the top of the hill the stranger jumped off and ran into the woods. Hardly able to breathe, the horseman got to the bottom of the hill and made it into Inez. When he rode into town he was barely able to speak. People who knew him saw that every hair on his head had turned from black to white. I asked Grandpa "Do you think that might have been the same strange man who jumped on the wagon?" "Who knows for sure, nobody knows for sure," he said.

Chapter 6
Wandering Stidham Man

We had someone wandering around up and down our road. Once, a man was trying to get into the front door of Grandpa's store. Grandpa and Mama were upstairs over the store sleeping but the rattling of the door awakened Grandpa. He went to the window that was directly over the door of the store and began to raise the window. The man down below looked up and saw that Grandpa was looking down at him and fled off down the road.

One night my first cousin Vonda was sitting in her living room watching television but had a strange feeling. She felt like somebody was behind her staring at her. She turned around and pulled back the curtain and saw a man's face two inches from her screened in window looking directly at her! She let out a scream and pulled the curtains back together. Her dad, brother and other family members were inside the house. Immediately her father grabbed his shotgun and went outside to find the window peeper but he had fled.

At the age of about 12, I was home alone watching television. I always turned up the television as loud as I could because I was nervous staying home by myself. However, I couldn't stand going to church and would rather have sat home alone and terrified than go to church. Suddenly I heard someone knocking loudly on the front door. I wasn't expecting anybody. The evening was too young for Mom and Dad to be home. I decided I wouldn't answer the door. The knock got louder as if the person was banging on the door. I was terrified and went to the back bedroom and picked up the shotgun. The gun was a single shot 12-gauge and I quickly dropped the barrel and shoved a shell into the chamber.

I went back to the living room barely able to walk because I was shaking. The visitor had moved to the back door and began banging on the back door as though he was trying to break it down. I sat on the sofa of the living room hoping he would give up and leave. This apparently was not going to happen and soon he was back at the front door pounding as hard as he could. I had reached my limit and lifted the shotgun up and aimed at the door. My mother had once said that if someone was trying to break into our house to just shoot through the door. Looking back, our door was so thick the pellets would have probably just bounced off it and hurt me. I prepared to pull the trigger but decided against it.

I knew I had locked the storm door and decided I would walk over and open the big wooden door and talk through the storm door. I would take my gun and put it beside the door in case the man tried to get through the storm door. Opening the door I did not recognize the man but he asked "Is Walt home?" Trying to keep my composure I replied. "No sir, he has gone to church." "Does he still have some hogs for sale? I've been wanting to buy some hogs from him," the man said. "Yes sir I believe he does but you will have to talk to him about that. He should be home in about an hour." "Okay, I'll check back with him." The man walked off the porch and I closed the wood door. I heard a car start and pull out of the driveway.

When Dad came home I told him about the visitor. He was clueless about who it could have been. I'm clueless about whether he ever came back and bought any hogs. Before going to bed

Dad asked, "I bet you were scared weren't you?"

White Man in the House

Occasionally, I would feel a bit strange in the old white house on Stidham. When I was a child I had climbed into bed with my parents and looked into the living room and noticed a white man walking through the living room and looking back in my direction. I never saw him again. But up until I left home, I almost never went to sleep in the back bedroom of the house without hearing a tapping noise on the bed where I slept.

When I was younger I would be up and down turning on the light to see if I could see anything. I would often inspect the bed but could never determine anything about the bed that would make a noise. Moving the bed to another place in the bedroom seemed to help but there were times I would still hear the tapping sound on the headboard of my bed. By the time I was 14 I gave up paying any attention to it and would often go to sleep without really giving it much thought. This was the same bedroom my mama Mollette died in when I was not quite four years old.

Chapter 7
The Screaming Bullfrog

A fried frog leg is tasty. I ate some frog legs at a young age but had never been frog gigging.

When I was a young teenager we had bullfrogs all up and down the creek on Stidham. At night the sound of bullfrogs would almost be like a concert. They were beautiful to listen to in the evening.

Buz and I decided we would go bullfrog gigging one night. We found gigs and feed sacks to carry them in and waded into the creek about 9:00. I had never done this before but Buz told me what to do. "Just shine your light on the creek bank and look for their eyes. Listen to see where the croaking is coming from and shine your light in that direction. When you see one, gig it and put it in your sack."

We parked our bicycles close to my uncle's bridge and got into the water. The creek was about a foot deep at this time of the year. We waded down past our bridge and then back up past Junior's bridge. It was not that far but was a nice wade in the creek. Bullfrogs were everywhere. We each caught over 20 bullfrogs. Our sacks were full. One particular frog was not happy about being in my sack. I was clueless about which one it was but I suspected it was the giant one that I had gigged and almost never got into my sack. The sound coming from my sack was like a woman screaming bloody murder! Bloody murder!

I knew the frog was inside my sack and could not possibly escape. Finally after gigging all the frogs we wanted, Buz and I climbed out of the creek and were wet up above our knees. We tied up our sacks and started riding our bikes down the road. Between Junior's bridge and our bridge the frogs made a lot of noise and Buz was still a mile away from his house. Buz continued home with his sack of frogs dangling from his handlebars. I held onto my sack as I crossed the bridge home with my one screaming frog.

My mom and dad had gone to bed so I took my frogs and put them in the smoke house and closed the door. I went in and changed clothes and went to bed. Occasionally, I could hear that frog still screaming.

The next day my dad cut off the legs of the frogs and prepared them for frying. Later that day we had a big pan of fried frog legs and they were oh so good. As I was eating I wondered if I was eating the screaming frog.

Chapter 8
One Big Snake

I wandered off into the hills once when I was five years old and got lost. I had no sense of direction at that time. I wandered around the hill behind our house and eventually wound around the hill behind my uncle Junior's house and up to Uncle Sebern's house. I was not that far away from home, but I couldn't tell where I was.

My mother realized I had wandered off and looked everywhere for me. She eventually got into her car and drove to Uncle Junior's asking if they had seen me. They had not. While she was at Junior's I was about 100 yards up on the hill from their house and was trying to walk down the hill when suddenly a snake seemed to stand up three feet in the air. To a five-year-old it looked like a monster. I turned and started running up the hill hollering for my mother. When you are five years old and need help the first word you scream is "Mommy!!!"

My mother heard my screaming and could not figure out where the sound was coming from but thought maybe it was in the direction of our house. She drove back home. Eventually I was able to spot Uncle Junior's house from the hill and made my way there without getting attacked by the snake.

When I arrived there I was covered with dirt and leaves from tramping through the hills. My first cousin Johnny said, "You are in trouble. Your mother has been looking for you and is she ever mad!" I immediately left and headed for home. When I arrived my mother immediately spanked me and put me in the bed.

Once, I was crossing our bridge and a big black snake was wiggling across it. I took off toward the house running. My mother saw me running home. She asked me what was wrong I said, "There is a big snake on the bridge." She went to the garage, grabbed a hoe, and went out to the bridge and killed it.

Later I would watch a black snake and a green snake fight underneath that bridge. The black snake won. The black snake swallowed the green snake. Both snakes appeared to be three or more feet long.

Chapter 9
Light on the Porch

We had a light on the front porch of our house. My mother would always turn it on when I was across the creek at Grandpa and Mama's place. When leaving their store at 8:00 it was already dusk. I would focus my eyes on the porch light. The light on the porch would guide me in the right direction so that I could see how to walk across our bridge and down the lane.

As I grew older and would come home late from playing basketball games or going to church my mother left the front porch light on. When I got home I always turned the light out on the porch. I was always glad to round the curve and look up ahead and across our creek to see that the porch light was on.

Many years later I would come home around that curve with a wife and two sons. If I arrived later in the day the porch light would be burning. My mom and dad were expecting us. The light on the porch always looked so good.

In the later years of my life I have always tried to keep the light burning when my children or other family members are on their way home.

Chapter 10
Hitchhiking

We never forget the people who invest time in our lives. From the fourth grade and through high school I had the opportunity to be involved in school basketball. Getting home from practice was always another story. During elementary school and junior high I could normally depend on my mother, Don Ward or James Webb. Virgil Moore was also good to see that I had a ride home.

High school was a little different and there were a few times during my freshman and sophomore years that I would hitchhike back to Milo. Ball practice would normally last at least an hour or two past normal school bus times. My dad's work schedule or my mother's schedule did not allow them to be at school for a pickup.

I wasn't the only person to ever stand on the bridge leading out of Inez and thumb for a ride. I was never afraid to get into a car with anybody and never dreamed of any danger. Cars would pass by. I would continue to stand and wait for the next car. One would approach and I would try to look friendly. After all, how menacing can a skinny 14 or 15-year-old look?

Having a large family in the county at that time helped. I remember Uncles Sebern, Junior, Haskell and other relatives picking me up. Most of the time it would be a total stranger and usually the stranger would drive out of their way to drop me off on Milo at the bridge leading to our house.

My dad's work schedule changed during my sophomore year. I remember that really helped since he was coming through town about the same time as I was getting out of practice. He would wait near the old Chevy dealership across from the Baptist Church to pick me up.

Looking back I never had to walk home once. When I was a young teenager I ran from Milo to Inez a few times for exercise but I never once had to walk home from basketball practice. God always made a way.

Chapter 11
Buzzard Rock

Several of us living on Milo enjoyed playing on Buzzard Rock. I heard that years ago my first cousin Eugene gave the giant rock formation its name because he saw some buzzards flying around the rock.

The giant rock formation could be easily seen before the foliage came into bloom. From our bridge on Milo there is a direct view of the rock. During the summer the rock is more difficult to see.

Buzzard rock was one neat place to hang out and look down on the world. We could see everywhere it seemed. Once we climbed on top of the rock there were small chasms to jump across.

One chasm involved literally pressing your back against one rock and then pushing your feet against another rock and walking yourself up. Finally, getting on top of one rock required a jump of about four to five feet across to get to the next rock formation. This wasn't a bad jump but the next jump was more dangerous. If you didn't make that jump there would be a bad 15 to 20 feet fall into the rocks.

As 10 and 12-year-olds it had to be done. Buz, Kevin, Slim Daddy and any of us who played on the rock cliff would eventually have to gut it out and make those jumps. You simply felt that if you didn't man up and do it, you would walk home as a wimp.

There was certainly no way to calculate how far we had to jump across the chasm. The width looked to be about five feet. But there was no way to measure and no one to this day knows exactly the width of the chasm. We all risked our lives many times to jump across that chasm on Buzzard Rock.

Chapter 12
Brown Chevy Station Wagon

There were seven of us in our family. This included my dad, Walter (Walt), Mom (Eula), Geneva, Wanda, Arvel, Clyde and me.

The earliest car I can remember was our brown 1958 Chevy station wagon. The station wagons were the mini-vans of that era. There was a front seat and then two more bench seats behind. Each bench would seat three people, even the front seat.

All seven of us were in that car a couple of times that I remember. I know we made at least one trip to Columbus, Ohio and visited with Mom's brother Clyde and his wife Ellen. They had two sons, Kenneth and Dennis. Since I was four or five years old I was squished in the middle of one of the benches. For awhile I would be between Mom and Dad on the front bench. Then I would be on the second seat and finally in the back row.

I was four or five at the time and everyone else was 10 to 14 years older than me. I was born almost 10 years behind Clyde who had been the baby of the family until I came along.

Another place we visited was Whitesville, West Virginia. Mama Mollette had been married to Steve Hall and they produced four sons and one daughter. Steve died and she married Lafe Mollette producing Willard and my dad, Walter. Lafe had a daughter by a previous marriage. Her name was Alka.

We would go to West Virginia and spend the night with one of Dad's brothers. We would either spend the night with Russell and Lou or Elbert and his wife Opal.

Riding in that brown station wagon around East Kentucky and the West Virginia mountain roads for three or four hours was always a test of patience and perseverance on everybody's part. Plus, we always made those trips in the summer and we did not have air conditioning.

Even in 1959 there was nothing hot about that brown Chevy wagon. It was a station wagon. But Dad bought it new and eventually he also had an old Chevy truck. When Mama died in 1958 we only had one car and that day the car was gone with Dad and his mining buddy because it was his turn to drive. Having only one car that day was tough when my mother wanted to try to take Mama Mollette to the hospital.

Since I was 21 years old I have tried to keep two cars. I figured out at a young age that I never knew when one would be out of commission or in use and that second car might come in handy.

Chapter 13
We Had an Outside Toilet

It was common on Stidham for families to have outside bathrooms. They weren't really bathrooms but simply toilets. They were simply wooden versions of what we see at many public events today known as Porta Potties or portable toilets. Ours was made of wood. Most of the people who lived up and down Stidham, or what became known as Milo, had toilets or "outhouses" as some called them. Eventually I called our outside toilet the "Johnny House."

I am fortunate that I cannot recall a time when we did not have a bathroom with a shower inside our house. We were blessed. We did maintain the outside toilet and were glad to have it. After all, there were those moments with seven people in the house that somebody else needed the bathroom and the little outside Johnny House came in handy.

It was a great place to catch up on reading. We always had a Sears or JC Penney's catalog or two out there. As a small child it was a bit difficult for me because the triangle hole that was cut in the toilet was too big for me and I was worried about falling through the hole. I also worried about what was in that toilet. It was simply a little tiny building built over a four or five-foot hole and what was dropped down into that hole stayed in that hole. It did not come back up.

I was terrified that if I fell down through that toilet hole nobody would ever find me. And, even if they did, they would not want to lift me out of that place. I also feared the mountain creatures. Occasionally we would see mice like everybody else but in Appalachia you have lizards, lots of spiders, bugs, frogs and snakes. Black snakes and green snakes are common and occasionally you will see or hear of somebody seeing a copperhead or rattlesnake.

One night we were coming back from church at about 10:00. I was in the back seat lying down with my face toward the back windshield looking at the beautiful moonlit sky and enjoying a sky full of stars in the clear Appalachian hills. We were driving up the hill from Route 40, which is the beginning of Milo, leading up the hill to Dead Man's Curve. Suddenly my dad hit the brakes of his car and I slammed against the back of his seat and ended up in the floorboard. Suddenly he put the car in reverse and backed up hurriedly. The lights of the car shone on the road and there was a big snake! I got out of the car with my dad and we walked toward it. It was a huge rattlesnake. It looked to be at least six feet long. It had been either crossing the road or simply enjoying the warm pavement. Obviously the snake was dead.

"Son we may have saved somebody's life tonight" said Dad. If somebody had come walking through there they would never have survived the bite of that snake. We got back in the car with the picture of that big snake forever etched in my mind.

Critters exist in the hills of East Kentucky. I never saw a snake in or around the toilet and I never wanted to. We kept the outside toilet. Even after everybody left home and the bathroom of the house was newly remodeled. After all, you never know when you might need that Johnny House.

Chapter 14
Tonsil Surgery

Tonsillitis was a way of life for me as a child. Every three or four months my throat was sore from swollen tonsils.

Mama Hinkle was a fan of Oral Roberts. In the fifties and sixties, Oral Roberts was a big name. He and Billy Graham were among the first to utilize national radio and television. Mama must have occasionally sent a few dollars to Oral as she had one of his books and a few of his trinkets.

One day Mama had Oral on the radio. He was preaching his passionate message on faith healing. It got close to the end of his program and it was time for his prayer of healing. This was where he prayed for everybody to be healed.

"Glenn" called Mama, "come over here and put your hands on the radio." I got a little nervous. "Okay, Mama." Walking over to the old brown radio she took my hands and put them on the radio. Oral was in full prayer mode for healing. He had asked people to touch the radio as a point of contact to be healed. As Oral prayed, Mama prayed that I would be healed of tonsillitis. Mama prayed a passionate prayer. I stood there spellbound by it all. My mind was blank as I just took in the prayer.

When the prayer was over Mama said "Glenn, you may never be sick again from tonsillitis." I was, and many more times.

Occasionally, I used to stay with Mama and Grandpa. Often they would sleep over their store. They had several beds upstairs all in one open room and I thought it was really cool. Mama had a bed and Grandpa had a bed. There was a half bed that I slept in and I seem to recall there was even another bed.

The half bed was just a few feet from Mama's bed. One night she wanted to teach me a prayer. She talked about the importance of prayer and that I should pray each night before I went to sleep. "Glenn, repeat these words after me. Now I lay me down to sleep. I pray the Lord my soul to keep. If I should die before I wake I pray the Lord my soul to take." It was something like that. I wasn't used to doing this and it made me a bit nervous.

With continuing bouts of tonsillitis my mom and dad began talking to me about surgery. "You need to get those tonsils out of there." Dad would say. Doctors were scary because my only experience was with Doc Ford in Inez. Doc Ford was the only doctor in Martin County. Whenever my mother took me to see him it was for a shot and shots always hurt. He always gave me a shot in the butt. I was five or six years old and he would lay me across my mother's lap. I would scream, cry and kick every time he gave me a shot.

Going to the doctor wasn't very much fun. However, it seemed easier in some ways than today. Doc Ford kept his own pharmacy in a room beside his office. He would always go back and fix a little packet of pills for us to take home after he saw us. There were no trips to the pharmacy in those days. We didn't have to call our insurance company to ask if it was okay. The doctor gave us the medicine. We paid him a dollar or two and we were out the door.

Even as a child, I was always trying to make deals. Mom and Dad would talk about me having my tonsils cut out and I started negotiating. If I got my tonsils taken out then maybe I could get a pony. I thought having a pony would be awesome. I suggested that if the pony did not work out then a new bicycle and $5.00 to boot would be just as good. Mom and Dad promoted the idea of a bicycle since they knew that feeding and caring for a pony would be a long haul proposition.

We visited with a surgeon at the Paintsville Hospital and scheduled me for the next morning. The worst part was being put to sleep with a combination of ether and gas. It felt like I was smothering to death. With a mask strapped to my face there was nothing to do but inhale. Within four or five breaths I began to feel as if I was being pushed down the road with no way to turn around.

A couple of hours later I woke up and it was over. For some reason I was crying. The doctor said that was probably just my response to the anesthesia. In the olden days, this was about 1961 or 1962, they kept you in the hospital until you were on your way to being well. I stayed three nights in the hospital. This is unheard of today for a tonsillectomy.

The next weekend we were shopping for a new bicycle. The local Western Auto had bicycles and I picked out a pretty red one that had a horn. I didn't know how to ride a bike so my dad bought training wheels. Even with the training wheels I probably wrecked that bike in the gravel no less than 50 times the first couple of days of ownership.

The next part of the deal was the $5.00. Mom and Dad gave me $5.00 because I had the surgery. The following weekend we were in Paintsville, Kentucky at my favorite place to eat, the GC Murphy snack counter. They had great fountain cokes, hotdogs and hamburgers. We all had hotdogs and drinks. I had two hotdogs and when it was time to pay the ticket I used my

$5.00 to treat Mom and Dad to lunch. I even had a buck and some change left over.

I would go on to have an occasional sore throat or virus just like everybody else. I never again had another bout with tonsillitis. The tonsils were gone. Good healthcare is essential for all. We should have regular checkups and take ownership of our health. I'm glad the surgeon could so easily remove my tonsils. He helped me.

Putting it all into perspective though I can see where Mama's prayer was answered.

Chapter 15
Neighbors Across the Creek

Stidham lost its name to Milo throughout the years. Few people today would even remember the little post office that was run by Grandpa Hinkle out of his grocery store. The postal system did away with the Stidham Post Office and our address became Tomahawk even though the road was commonly called Milo. Further down our road there was a little Milo Post Office that in time was eliminated as well.

Milo was a gravel road. Up on Route 40 the road was paved and it felt like a super highway coming off rocky and dusty Milo. Whenever a car drove down Milo dust would spread almost all the way to our house which sat about 100 yards from the road. On a hot summer day dust seemed to travel and it would eventually reach our front porch.

We had a front porch with a wooden swing and a metal glider. Four large trees were in front of the house. One was a big apple tree. The trees provided incredible shade from the beaming afternoon sun.

One summer day Geneva, Wanda and Josephine, our first cousin, were rocking back and forth on the wooden swing. I climbed up on the side of the swing and was standing holding on to the chain that ran up into the ceiling. I felt like Tarzan. After about five minutes of holding four people the swing gave way and we all ended up on the porch floor.

We didn't have air conditioning. We had a fan. On 100 degree days, the fan barely made a dent in the heat. We just drank a lot of water and Kool-Aid. Kool-Aid was about five cents a pack and would make a quart. With five kids in the house it was the most financially feasible way to quench our thirst.

The community was small. Family lived all around. Grandpa, Mama and James lived across the road to the right of us. The Roland family lived across the road to the left. To the north of us was family. All of the relatives living to the north of us were Hinkles. They were my mother's brothers. Sebern and Velma, John C. and Lucille, Haskel and Maude, plus all of their children, who were my first cousins, lived to the north of us on Milo. Visiting all of these people gave me something to do as a kid. My aunts, uncles and first cousins were all great to me.

The Roland people were not blood family. We knew them but there was never any socializing with them. As a child I remember being afraid of them. Mr. Roland was a big guy who rode a motorcycle. His wife was skinny and frail.

One day Mom and I were sitting in the living room of the house looking out the picture widow across the porch. We saw Mrs. Roland run out of the house, but then Mr. Roland ran out and grabbed her. Mrs. Roland seemed distressed. I was about five years old at the time. I could see the concern in my mom's face. About five minutes later Mrs. Roland bolted out of her house and was sprinting down the gravel Milo Road. Big Mr. Roland was right behind her, caught her and began leading her back to the house. This was scary stuff.

I don't remember much after that. We didn't have a telephone at that time. There was no way to communicate that someone might have been in danger. My mother walked out into the yard as if making her presence visible might be a deterrent to Mr.

Roland. That possibly saved Mrs. Roland's life.

Appalachian people on Milo were overall good about minding their own business. People might have talked about other people but we didn't know that much about everybody. Unlike today, people were not in everybody's business with social media, computers, cell phones, etc. We really didn't know what occurred in the houses across or down the road.

A week or so later my mother got a bad report from Mama telling us that Mrs. Roland had banged on her door after midnight begging for help. Mrs. Roland had literally jumped through a window of her house to escape from her violent husband. According to Mama she was cut in multiple places from the window glass. Mama spent over an hour bandaging Mrs. Roland's injuries. Mama and Grandpa did not have a telephone at this time either.

We had neighbors all over Milo but yet we still were very isolated. This is why most people had guns. My dad had several shotguns. He used them to squirrel and rabbit hunt but they were also for protection. There was no hope of help from the local county sheriff if we were threatened. We had no way to call anyone. It was up to us to protect ourselves.

I don't know what happened to the Rolands. They eventually moved away. I don't know if Mrs. Roland ever got away from her husband or not. Maybe life totally got better for them and everything turned out peaceful and great. There was not any communication about them between any of our family. Some time later, there was a rumor that Mr. Roland had died in a motorcycle crash.

Chapter 16
The Peach Tree

We had a lot of nice trees around our house when I was a kid. A large peach tree was in our backyard. The peaches from the tree were delicious but I can remember some uncomfortable moments. On several occasions my mother took me to the peach tree, broke off a limb and took that limb right across my legs and behind.

On several occasions, my dad used his belt on me. Once when I was four or five years old I woke him during one of his day naps. He worked in an underground mine all night and he slept in a little bedroom behind our house that he and Mom had fixed in what we called the smokehouse. On one summer day I made too much noise and woke him up. He whipped me until I thought I was going to die.

Sitting on the living room couch sobbing profusely, I remember becoming terrified of my dad. I certainly never wanted anything like that to happen again and so I grew up very conscious of trying to never make him mad. There were other occasions during my childhood when I got the belt or his hand on my bottom.

Standing and being whipped by a peach tree limb didn't seem right so I started moving away from the swing of the limb. Mom quickly improvised and started holding me by one arm as she whipped me. One day Mom took me by the arm and led me out to the peach tree and I started begging her to let me stand just a few feet from the tree. If I could just coax her into letting me go then I would make a run for it. She never fell for it and kept a tight grip on my wrist. While I eventually started trying to escape from Mom I could never break the tight grasp she would have on my wrist.

Most adults look back in retrospect understanding that some of the spankings they received as kids may have been deserved or maybe not deserved. I'm sure I deserved a few of them. There were a couple along the way that were totally unnecessary. Not too many of us look back on being whipped and remember those times as fond moments. They never endeared my parents to me. I certainly knew my parents would not put up with anything that was disorderly or disrespectful. I knew that when they told me no, they meant no.

When I was about four I had opened the door that led out to the front porch. Suddenly there was a stampede coming through the house. My brothers Arvel and Clyde were hollering every breath "Hold that door open Glenn! Hold that door open!" Mom was chasing them from the kitchen through the dining room with a peach limb switch and now they were in the living room. Mom was swinging the switch at them and they were trying to escape. Obediently I stood there holding the door as they came through to the open-air front porch and then leaped over the banister in escape.

By the time I was nine or ten years old the big peach tree in the back yard was falling apart. The limbs were breaking off into the yard and I think Dad feared it might break over in a strong wind and fall on our house. A couple of men showed up one day, cut it down and hauled it off. I never missed that peach tree.

Chapter 17
Drinking Beer

Dad became different after he started going to church with Mom. For a number of years during my childhood there was a lot about my dad that I loved. I remember sitting in his lap sleeping for over an hour in front of the coal burning stove. I've often reflected on the times that we would put Old Blue, our hound dog, in the back of the truck on Sunday afternoons and go for a truck ride, just the two of us. As a child I remember literally almost walking on his heels as I tried to keep up with him. Wherever he went I wanted to go. After a few whippings, scoldings and stern remarks I gave that up.

On Sundays we would be out in the backyard with the shotgun shooting cans or watching for a squirrel to shoot. Mom would come out into the backyard and ask Dad if he wanted to go to church "No, I don't believe so," he would respond. Mom wanted Dad to go to church with her. Eventually he would and it did make a difference in our home.

In my early childhood years I remember beer in the refrigerator. I drank a lot of soft drinks. Grandpa and Grandma's grocery store was just across the creek and down the road. Soft drinks and candy bars were always accessible. Those cold cans of beer in the refrigerator looked like a Pepsi, RC or Coke. I saw Dad drinking them and I wanted one too. Mom and Dad didn't want me to touch a beer. One day I finally talked my dad into letting me drink a beer. He popped the top, handed it to me and I took a big swig like I was drinking lemonade. Out the back door

I went gagging and spitting and trying to get that out of my mouth.

I believe that broke me from becoming a drinker. Many of my acquaintances drank some in high school. I even tried it again when I was about 13 or 14. Some of my buddies, who I ran around with on Milo Road, were drinking some and I wasn't being very cool by not drinking. One of my buddies brought me a couple of beers one day and I hid them in one of Dad's buildings. They would usually drive over to Inez or someplace on Saturdays and so I figured I could down a beer while they were gone. One Saturday I spent about three hours trying to drink one beer and I couldn't do it. I couldn't stand the taste.

I also developed a fear of alcohol at a young age. My dad gave it up when he started going to church. He then started warning about the danger and destructive nature of alcohol abuse. I never saw beer or wine in our house again during my childhood days. Intoxicated people always scared me as a child. They were out of control, said crazy stuff and did crazy things.

One time Dad, Mom and I drove up the road to visit one of our neighbors. We pulled up in the front yard and his wife came out to talk with us. Her husband never came out. Dad asked, "Where is he?" "Well, Walt he's in the bed drunk." Dad shook his head. A few moments later he hollered for her to bring the bottle but she responded that it was empty. With that he let out a curse word and then seemed to pass out. That made an impression on me.

We didn't smoke cigarettes, but most of Mom's brothers smoked. They visited us regularly so Mom always kept an ashtray handy. In those days it was not congenial to tell people to take their cigarettes out of the house. My uncles on my mom's side of the family would visit, sit down for an hour and chat while lighting up one cigarette after another.

Mom and Dad railed at us about smoking. They did not want any of us kids to smoke. Smoking never appealed to me either.

Chapter 18
Splitting My Head Wide Open

Sunday afternoons were filled with family visits. We camped out at Mama's and Grandpa's a lot of Sunday afternoons. This was the day the store was closed. After six long days of tending to the store they deserved a day off.

However, I can remember numerous times when Grandpa would open the doors for the family who were there. Sometimes it might be 10 or 15 people.

It only took two families to show up to make up a large gathering. If Sebern and his family came that was six, then add John C. Jr. and his family and you have another six plus Mama and Grandpa and James. It adds up to 15 people really quickly. Plus I was riding my bicycle then and it only took me 10 seconds to be across the road and sitting on Grandma's porch.

When Grandpa opened the store on Sunday afternoons for the family gang, everybody paid for what they bought or charged. I think that most of us had credit accounts. When I charged something it was on my mom and dad's credit account. I knew I could get by with 15 to 20 cents a day of expenditures. I could buy a Dr. Pepper and maybe even a bag of nuts or a candy bar. I knew I would be in good shape as long as I could at least get a cold pop on a hot day.

On Sundays, the store would only be open for about 30 minutes. Grandpa may have made a little money and we all had some refreshments. After this it was back out to the front porch where we sat in the swings and wooden chairs until everyone decided to go home. There never seemed to be a rush. On some of those Sunday afternoon's it felt like time stood still. There was a fellowship on that front porch unlike any other that I've experienced in this life.

Mom's sister Kathleen came quite often with her husband Bill and children Shelby and Mose. Shelby was closer to my brother's age and although Mose was closer to my age he was still about four years older than me. Mose was tall. He was about 6'6" or 6'7" and was not fragile but he was a gentle guy.

Mom, Dad and I went over to Warfield to visit with them several times. Mose was great about trying to entertain me if he was around. We played in a little building out behind their house that they used for storage. There were a couple of chairs, tools, canned foods, junk, ropes and stuff that was stored in the building.

For some weird reason Mose and I decided we would entertain ourselves by tying each other up with the ropes. Mose sat down in one of the cane bottom chairs and I tied him up first. I was about seven at the time. He quickly shook off the ropes and was out of the chair. Next was my turn and within a few minutes I wiggled out and was free. Mose sat down again and this time I tied him up a little better but within a few minutes he was free from the ropes and standing up smiling. We kept this going and then came his turn to tie me up again.

On this next go around Mose did a better job at tying the ropes and knots very securely. When he was finished tying, it was obvious I wasn't going anywhere. On the previous tie up I had been able to move a little and the ropes loosened. My thought was "I'll try to stand a little and maybe that will loosen the ropes." As soon as I began to go up on my toes the chair tipped over and my head hit the wooden door that led to the entrance. The whack against the door barely hurt at first. It was a wood door with wooden panels going across the door. My head hit one of the wooden panels. Mose got out of the room fast. "I'm going for help." he exclaimed. I was a little uncomfortable. I was "hogtied" as we used to say. My head was leaning up against the door but I wasn't in pain. In my peripheral vision, I could see a nice big pool of blood forming underneath my face.

I heard voices coming out of the house. I could hear Mose leading my mom and dad and his mom and dad, Kathleen and Bill. "Be careful opening the door his head is right against it." Slowly my dad came into that little building and saw that my head was split open and blood was going everywhere. He pulled the chair and me back away from the door. He started trying to untie me but couldn't do it. "Look at how these knots are tied!" he said.

Dad always carried a knife and pulled out a Hawkeye and began quickly cutting at the ropes to set me free. Kathleen ran back to the house and came out with several towels. She and Mom started wrapping my head trying to stop the bleeding. Dad finally got the ropes off me cutting in several places. "I've never seen a tie-up like this before." he exclaimed.

My head was obviously numbed from the impact but I was starting to feel it. Dad picked me up and carried me to the car and placed me in the back seat. He, Mom and I sailed out of the driveway and toward Warfield. There were no medical emergency places close by so Dad drove the 13 miles around winding curvy mountain roads to Inez where we pulled up to the funeral home. "Well, I guess it's over." I thought.

Dad jumped out of the car and within minutes a man from the funeral home was with him. "I'm shaking too bad," he told the man "can you drive him?" The man pulled a hearse around and he and Dad loaded me onto the gurney. Within five minutes I was riding in the back of a hearse toward Paintsville Hospital.

We did not have 911 in 1962. We did not have a hospital or medical emergency center in our county. There was no such entity as a paramedic team. A funeral home hearse was all that was available. I'm sure that on that day Mom and Dad were glad it was available.

I held on to the gurney as we drove over two winding mountains on the old road to Paintsville from Inez. I was taken to the emergency room where I laid for about 30 minutes. A doctor came in and he with the nurse began cleaning my wound. I could feel that process and it stung. He started stitching the cut and when it was over I had 23 stitches in my head.

I spent the night in the hospital. Between the emergency room care and overnight in the hospital the cost was less than $100. Dad had health insurance from the coal mine where he worked and he was a member of the United Mine Workers Association. Mom and Dad were always glad that they had good health insurance from the mines. Dad would never work for a mine unless it was a union mine.

I looked like a victim of war for a few days as I wore a bandage. Mom and Dad let me stay out of school for three or four days. Then, I had to go back with a shaved head and 23 stitches. I was not exactly a beautiful sight. I wore a baseball cap but a couple of the older boys on the bus were relentless about me removing my cap so they could see the stitches. By the time I got to school I just gave it up and took off my cap and walked around school with a head full of stitches. That was only for a couple of days and then we were back at the doctor's office to have them removed.

Mose and I never played in the little building out behind his house again. Actually, I don't think Mose and I played together much at all after that. Maybe Bill or Kathleen scolded him. I hope they didn't. We were just being boys. I'm sure he was in a state of shock for a long time afterwards. I think that every time he saw me he felt bad about what happened. I hope not. Neither of us ever dreamed that one of us might get hurt. We were just being kids.

Chapter 19
Two Sisters and Two Brothers

I was blessed with four siblings named Geneva, Wanda, Arvel and Clyde. I was born far behind them all. I was behind Geneva by almost 14 years, Wanda by 13 years, Arvel by 11 years and Clyde by almost 10 years. For nine years and eight months Clyde was the baby of the family. And then one day I came along.

I wasn't a planned baby. Mom was 38 when I was born. She could have elected to have an abortion but such things weren't that commonly performed in 1955. I was blessed with two parents who had the ability to suck it up and move on with life.

Wanda tells me that I was Mommy's baby which I guess means that she doted on me a lot. I think she did especially up until I was about three years old. She kept me in the baby bed in the front room where she and Dad slept. Often, if I started crying she would pick me up and put me right between them. This only worked for a while for everyone involved.

My adventure with brothers and sisters was short-lived. Wanda married when I was five and moved to Columbus, Ohio. Geneva married when I was six and moved to Inez, Arvel married when I was about seven and soon thereafter moved to Mansfield, Ohio. Clyde left home to attend Morehead State University when I was eight.

At the age of eight I suddenly became an only child except when Clyde came home from college, which was almost every weekend. My mother washed and ironed his clothes. He would usually come in Friday and Mom would have something for him to eat. I would hang close to him because I wanted to hear about college life and what he had to say about basketball. He was an honorable mention all state basketball player and I highly respected his opinion about basketball. Besides, by this time I was alone all week, except for the Monday through Friday school days. After school it felt like I was in an empty house and was different for a while. Having a big brother home on the weekends was nice.

I vaguely remember Wanda at home. I remember Mom, Dad and I going to the back of the courthouse to watch her dance. Behind the courthouse was a place where they would block off the streets, play records and occasionally have a band. One of our two pool halls was close to this and they offered a jukebox, billiards and an occasional fight. Scott Cline had a barbershop around the corner. Scott also had a small restaurant and a pool hall as well. When I was a kid and had a couple of nickels I enjoyed playing the pinball machines in Scott Cline's establishment.

I remember Wanda helping Mom around the house. I also remember her getting ready for her high school trip. The seniors took a trip to Washington, D.C. and rode by train. I remember her making sandwiches since everybody had to take food to eat.

These were days of true rural Appalachia America. We only had one way to get in and out of town at that time. The high school and the courthouse were the center of town. We also had the Village Restaurant. A high school friend Johnny and I loved to sneak off the high school campus and eat cheeseburgers at the Village Restaurant. They had a side room that was out of sight. Mr. Goble was the principal of the school at Inez. We were very uncomfortable that he would walk in and find us. Mr. Goble did not cut any slack. He was a strong disciplinarian. I was raised in the era when the paddle was commonly used.

We also had the Sweet Shop, two pool halls, a popular dairy bar and a restaurant that we called the Drive In. It was more of a family restaurant with a pool table. I don't remember people in the sixties having a lot of money. I do remember Inez being a clean little town with some business activity and lots of cars and people going through town.

Wanda began dating Glen Cline when I was only about four years old. It must have been love at first sight. I was happy that Glen came to see Wanda because I always enjoyed him coming. I know I was a pain for my older sister. She was trying to date and I wanted to be with them in everything that was going on. To make it worse, on Friday night, Saturday night or both, they would load up in Glen's car, drive across the bridge and leave me. Sometimes Glen would give me 15 cents or even a quarter and send me to Grandpa Hinkle's store. By the time I got back they had hightailed it out of the driveway, across the bridge and off to town for their evening date.

At the age of four I grew weary of being left behind. I searched one of Dad's buildings and found some nails. The next weekend while Glen and Wanda were in the house beginning their weekend date I got my nail and positioned it right under one of Glen's tires. I built a little sand dune around the nail with the sharp point headed right up toward the tire. All it would need was a little pressure from the right direction.

Sure enough about 30 minutes later they came out of the house all smiley and ready to leave the house. Since they were leaving me I just waved and went over to the edge of the house to see if my sand trap would work. It did. Glen backed right up on my nail and before he could drive down the driveway the tire was flat. I started looking for a place to disappear.

With the kind of whippings I had gotten from Mom and Dad in the past I didn't want to think about what kind of whipping I would get this time. No doubt Glen and Wanda were exasperated. Glen got out and changed the tire and they eventually went on their evening date. I don't really remember either of them saying too much to me that was hateful. From then on every time Glen and Wanda left the house he would walk around his car and check carefully for nails. He always found where I had set them.

Wanda and Glen married in August of 1960. They married in the front yard in front of the concrete steps that led up to our porch. A large crowd of family and friends gathered in our front yard for the ceremony. I stood on the top step with my mother who held on to my arm to keep me from getting in the middle of the wedding. When the wedding and kiss were finally complete and they were pronounced husband and wife I ran up to Wanda and said, "You didn't tell me you were going to do all of this."

The house was very festive that day. I don't know how many people actually attended the wedding but it seemed like 200 or more. We had a large family at that time with all the uncles, aunts and cousins. With friends we could easily have had that number of people or more.

People came and went through the house. We had simple refreshments of punch, mints and nuts and a lot of celebration. People were happy. I don't remember any pressure concerning who to invite and who not to invite, how much the wedding dress would cost, how much the reception would cost or any family animosity. It was a simple, wonderful good time through the eyes of a child.

Wanda and Glen drove off to start their new life. Several of the guys soaped their car with Just Married and many other inscriptions. A set of tin cans rattled as they drove down the driveway. They were off to Columbus, Ohio where Glen already had a job and they had a place to live. He was 21 and she was 18.

This was an era when kids left home at 17, 18 or 19. They went to Columbus, Ohio or Detroit, Michigan where there was plenty of work for people to do. They would get jobs and work for 30 years and be able to retire. Or, many would go to college at Morehead, Eastern or the University of Kentucky. They would spend four years in college, earn a degree and take care of themselves. Some would join the military but unfortunately most of the kids who went into the military were drafted and only stayed in the service for about two years.

When I was growing up very few of the kids ever dreamed of being in the military. All we saw were the horrors of Vietnam. That's all we knew or understood about military life. The military was not appealing during the Vietnam years.

Geneva married within about a year of Wanda's wedding. She had been dating Harold Buskirk for some time. Harold had actually been in the Army and spent a tour of duty in Germany. This was definitely more appealing than Vietnam.

Geneva was the first born and lived with Mom and Dad on the Hall Branch. Dad's brother Willard, his wife Opal and their family all lived on the Hall Branch in the same house with Mom, Dad and Geneva. This was where Dad lived with his dad Lafe and Mama Mollette. Up the hill from the house Lafe and Mama Mollette are buried. Close to this grave is a grave where Harvey, my first cousin, is buried. Harvey died at a young age of a gunshot wound. Harvey is the young man I previously mentioned who scored 30 to 40 points a basketball game when he was in the eighth grade.

Geneva attended the first grade while living on the Hall Branch but by her second year of school Mom and Dad had built the house on Stidham. I was about six when Geneva married and moved to a nice house in Inez.

When I was a child I was outside from sunup to sundown. We had a garden and farm animals and one year I remember a huge strawberry patch. For a while we had chickens. We had hogs, cows and a horse that I loved to ride. We also had one bathroom and seven people in the house. We had a shower until later Dad did some remodeling and added a bathtub.

One evening Mom was scolding us for having our feet on the furniture. Geneva had showered and responded "My feet are clean." I had been playing outside throughout the day. Even though I had probably been barefoot for most of the day I chimed in with Geneva "My feet are clean." Geneva scowled "Your feet are not clean!"

Geneva began teaching school at Grassy after her first semester of college at Morehead University. This was back in the days when the Board of Education would issue an emergency teaching certificate. For the next several years she would teach school and complete her degree at Morehead along with adding additional education later on.

I spent a lot of time at Geneva's house until I was about 16.

She and Harold lived in town and it gave me a chance to get off Milo for a Friday or Saturday night. When The Beatles aired on the Ed Sullivan show I watched all three Sunday night programs at their house because they could get CBS on their television. The only channel we could watch at home was NBC. We had an antenna that stretched all the way to the top of a mountain. We were lucky to get WSAZ out of Huntington, West Virginia. Geneva and Harold were always great to me.

Arvel married after Geneva. I was at Mama and Grandpa's store sitting in a cane bottom chair, probably sipping a Dr. Pepper. Mom came in to buy some groceries and said, "That Arvel just came home. He has slipped off and got married!"

We all went into shock because it was totally unexpected. Arvel and his first wife lived with us and with her parents for a couple of weeks until one day Arvel came in and packed a suitcase. He and his wife were off to Mansfield, Ohio. He started working in a factory and stayed there.

Arvel helped me learn how to ride a bicycle. That was a wonderful gift for a child who loved the freedom that came with riding a bike over miles of mountain roads.

Arvel came home around Christmas one year for just a few hours. He brought gifts for Mom and Dad but I couldn't find one gift he had brought for me. I eventually gave up walking around the house looking for a present. Before getting in his car to go back to Mansfield he opened the trunk of his car and came to the door and said "Glenn, here's a rod 'n reel for you for Christmas." It was very nice and I caught some fish out of the creek on Milo with that rod 'n reel. Arvel loved hunting, fishing and outdoor life as a kid and has all his life.

When I was a first and second grader, I was so glad that Arvel would sometimes be on the school bus. One day, one of the school bus bullies was picking on me and Arvel looked at him and said, "Leave him alone." The kid never bothered me again.

Clyde graduated from Morehead State University and married. Six months later while working as a manager trainee for Montgomery Ward in Portsmouth, Ohio he was drafted and sent off to Vietnam. I had the opportunity to dialogue with Clyde a bit more as a sibling since I was 12 before he graduated from college. I saw him about every weekend until he graduated from college and got married.

All of us left home for work, to pursue life or college by the time we were 18. We didn't want to sit at the house and expect Mom and Dad to take care of us. We knew there was a world outside of Milo. We knew this because we watched WSAZ television out of Huntington and NBC showed us each day what was going on in that world.

Actually, the world outside of Milo sometimes looked scary. All we saw on television were race riots going on in Alabama, reporters telling their stories from Vietnam and the death of John F. Kennedy, among other violence that accompanied the sixties.

But, we knew at that time there was very little to do in Martin County except teach school. The board of education was the largest employer in the county. Coal mining at that time was over in West Virginia. Dad drove almost two hours one way every day to Holden, West Virginia to scrap out a paycheck. The coal boom would eventually come to Martin County. It would not be until about 1971 that big mining and big money would come to the county.

My grandparents on both sides, my mom, dad, brothers and sisters all left home at young ages to become hard-working, self-sustaining, independent, productive Americans. They followed and lived the American dream of being free, independent and living the American life. They all grew up to have a strong faith in God, raised their families, supported their churches, worked long, stable years and eventually realized retirement.

Growing up on Milo wasn't a perfect world by any stretch of the imagination. Mom and Dad were not perfect people but they stayed with it, kept working, paid their bills, fed and clothed us and went to church. Mom and Dad weren't quitters.

I actually don't see how they survived. Dad was about 17 and Mom was 21 when they married. Dad did not start working in coal mining until he was 25. Once he started he stayed with it until he was 55 and then retired with a meager retirement check from the United Mine Workers. Eventually he received other checks from Social Security and other benefits that he was awarded due to the impact underground coal mining had on his health.

During their first nine years Dad worked odd jobs doing whatever he could to earn a paycheck. Somehow he and Mom made it, stayed married and raised five children. Mom died when she was 85. Dad would live almost five years and three months after mom died. He too died at the age of 85.

Chapter 20
Early Social Life

Grandpa and Grandma Hinkle's grocery store was the center of my social life. I always had a place to go as a child. In time, Mom trusted me to walk across our bridge and then about 100 yards down the road to the store. Finally after watching me all the way to the store a few times she grew relaxed about my journeys over to Mama and Grandpa's place.

The store was in plain sight of our house. You could look across the creek to the right of our house and the store and their house were in full view. You could see who was coming and going. But even in 1960 you couldn't just turn a child loose to roam up and down the road.

Sometimes I would stay too long at the store. I would sit in one of the cane bottom chairs and watch customers go in and out. I would buy a pop and sip on it and listen in on conversations as local people came and went.

I would always see family. Mom had four brothers who lived on Milo. Each brother was married with four to five children. Somebody from the family was always coming and going. James was usually around until I was about eight years old. Like my brother Clyde he went off to Morehead College after high school graduation and studied to become a teacher.

Later I would have James as my seventh and eighth grade teacher at Tomahawk Elementary School. He was even our basketball coach my eighth grade year. One of the best things that James did for our team, as an eighth grade basketball coach, was that he made us get into shape. We were the aerobic kids of the county. Nobody could run with us. During basketball practice, it was not unusual for us to run a solid hour of laps around the gym floor. I would sweat so much that when I would lie down on the gym floor to do sit-ups, a pond of sweat would form on my chest.

We had a fun season. We won most of our games but lost our final game in the county tournament by two points. I was almost 6'2" in the eighth grade and weighed 135 pounds. That means I was really skinny. My job was to get close to the basket and put the ball in the goal. In junior high, no one in the county was as tall as I was at that time. My job did not include dribbling the basketball and so I never worried about that part of the game.

Marvin Crisp was our star guard and ball handler. Marvin would score a lot of points and one night scored 27. In our final high school basketball game Marvin got under the basket and was knocked down while we were trying to rebound the basketball. He sprained his wrist and could not dribble the ball the rest of the game. This changed our entire game since we really did not have another ball handler. With eight seconds to go we were two points behind and James told me to bring the ball up the court. I didn't want to because I had never done that before.

I got the ball on the inbounds pass, dribbled it the entire length of the court; drove under the basket and made a layup. The crowd erupted in joy. I was ecstatic but turned to see one of the worst sights I had ever seen. The referee was rolling his arms. He called traveling with the basketball. The two points were nullified and the game was over. We lost.

Runner-up wasn't bad but we wanted to win. I learned early on that you win some and lose some. Marvin and I would go on to play basketball three years at Inez and then one year at Sheldon Clark High School. We were the first graduating class at Sheldon Clark in the 1972-73 school year.

James was a first cousin, almost like an older brother and mentor during my first eight years. I was always hanging out around the store and I'm sure I was a pain in the neck. He would take me up into the hills along with my first cousin Kevin and we would explore the beautiful nature of our surrounding mountains.

We also went squirrel hunting a couple of times. We squirrel hunted when I was about 12. James helped me shoot my first squirrel. We were back in the holler behind Grandma and Grandpa's house and suddenly we heard a squirrel on the side of a tree making a really weird sound. James said, "I'll walk down below the tree. That will make him move to your side of the tree and when he does, shoot him." I had never shot anything before.

James walked down the side of the hill and sure enough the squirrel started moving to my side of the tree. "Shoot him, shoot him!" James yelled. I raised my heavy 12-gauge shotgun took aim and "bang!" I got him. The squirrel fell to the ground. James laughed as I ran down the hill to find him.

Later my dad would skin that squirrel, fry it and eat it for dinner. Dad loved to eat squirrel, rabbit, groundhog, soft shell turtles, deer, etc. He always said he would eat about anything if it didn't eat him first.

James loved music. He was always the best banjo player in Martin County and probably one of the best in Kentucky. He taught me four or five chords on the guitar and three or four chords on the mandolin. That began my interest and love for music. James loved bluegrass music. That's the style that has permeated much of Kentucky back to the days of Bill Monroe who originated from Rosin, Kentucky. Loretta Lynn and Crystal Gayle were raised just in the next county, up the road from Paintsville where I was born. Ricky Skaggs was raised just a few miles from us in Lawrence County. If you've ever followed bluegrass music any then you get the picture of the area.

I used to sit for hours and listen to James, my brother Clyde who played the mandolin and guitar, Paul Fitzpatrick, Thomas Copley, and others play music. They would do shows and a guy by the name of Don Fannin would tell funny jokes in between the songs.

Paul had twin brothers named Garry and Larry. Larry played a bass fiddle, Garry the guitar and I knew a few chords on the mandolin. There were a few occasions that we got to perform at local shows before our older brothers performed. A couple of times we performed at intermission. We were about seven or eight years old at the time. It was a hoot.

In so many ways, it was a beautiful culture for a child to grow up in. We were isolated in Appalachia and we lived in our own world. Looking back it was a sweet place. The area didn't change much until I was about 14.

For many years, Grandpa had chest pains and suffered with periodic feelings of smothering. James told me that on many occasions his heart would get out of rhythm and Mama would pound him on the back to get his heart back in rhythm.

At the age of 83 Grandpa decided to check into the Louisa,

Kentucky hospital. To this day I can remember James and Grandpa pulling out of the parking lot of the grocery store. I had walked across the bridge and was walking in the direction of the store. James was driving and Grandpa appeared to be dressed up. I never saw him in a pair of jeans. He always looked neat and fully dressed as he waited on customers, pumped gas and tended the store.

As James drove down the road in a green '68 Ford 500 Galaxy I only saw Grandpa from the side and then the back of his head. It would be the last time I would ever see him. It was a curvy winding trip to Louisa from our house. It would take about 40 minutes. While my mom and dad went to see him, for some reason I was never on one of those trips.

Grandpa died in the hospital. James speculated that his heart got out of rhythm one night and Mama wasn't there to pound him on his back to get the rhythm back into order. I've always found it amazing that Grandpa and Mama worked in that store until he was 83 years old. He probably worked the day before he left the store to go to the hospital.

The store was something that he and Mama did together. It was a team effort. They fed themselves and raised 10 kids. They never had medical insurance. They paid cash for whatever they bought. When Grandpa died I'm told that he didn't have a lot of cash or savings.

James bought the 500 Ford Galaxy from Grandpa. James got a teaching job after college graduation and was clearing less than $400 a month. Grandpa told him, "You need a car and you're buying this one. You will pay me $300 a month." James did as he was told and completed paying him the total for the car just before Grandpa died.

Grandpa had put the money James paid him for the Ford behind the cigarette stand in the store. After his death the $3,600 was found there sacked away. "It was really about all he had." James said.

While Grandpa didn't die with a ton of cash he did die with a tremendous legacy and great integrity. He was a faithful, hard-working businessman. He owed nothing. He owned his business. He owned his house and property. He continued to care for himself and Mama until his dying day. He and Mama went to church at Sulphur Springs United Baptist but I don't remember him being in the thick of the business dealings of the church. I do remember him once sitting up front at the church.

At one time Grandpa owned a lot of land. I'm not sure how many hundreds of acres he had. Eventually he sold it off to sons Haskel, Seburn, John Jr. and my dad and mom. I believe I remember that my dad bought about 100 acres from him for about $1.00 an acre. This was sometime during the forties.

Martin County, Kentucky was known for a while as the poorest county in the United States. However, in the midst of extreme poverty Grandpa and Mama found a way to take care of themselves through the running of a tiny little country grocery. Grandpa even sold grocery items to people on credit. He allowed them to pay him "later." There was no collection effort and no interest charged on the credit. Our family even had a charge account but Dad settled up with him every Friday when he got his paycheck. I'm told there were numerous people that Grandpa never collected a dime from.

Grandpa and Grandma loved God and worked hard. They were faithful to God and each other. They didn't ask anyone to take care of them. Everybody took care of themselves. If you couldn't take care of yourself, then family and friends helped out.

Chapter 21
President Lyndon Johnson Comes to Martin County

I was in the third grade when our teacher Ilene Hinkle walked into the classroom and announced to our class that President John F. Kennedy had been shot. No one knew the details but someone had gotten the word that he had been shot. After riding the bus home I discovered from Mom that he was dead. For three to four days that's all we saw on television. From our one television affiliate channel we watched and heard details as the news story played out.

While visiting with Geneva and Harold, I saw Lee Harvey Oswald shot on live television. I do not remember the network we were watching. The police were walking with him handcuffed through a building when Jack Ruby stepped right into his path and shot him in the stomach.

Later, when I watched the replay of what happened on NBC all I could see was the long pistol barrel of Ruby's gun sticking out into the camera viewer. "Mom, Dad, that's Jack Ruby's gun!" I pointed as we all watched.

Milo Road and Martin County were a long way from Dallas, Texas and Washington, DC. We got a glimpse into the outside world through television but the unrest of our country seemed to be on another planet as far as we were concerned. We saw the racial riots, the ugliness of Vietnam and a Presidential assassination but miles of curvy roads made Martin county seem like a safe place.

In time our world would change. Lyndon Johnson who was the Vice President under Kennedy was sworn into office. In comparison to Kennedy he was very unimpressive. Kennedy was handsome, articulate and generated an outlook of optimism throughout the country. Johnson was older, less articulate and couldn't excite a lottery winner.

However, in 1964 Johnson came to Martin County and Inez, Kentucky. We were out of school that day but I didn't imagine that I would be going the four miles into Inez to see him. Mom and Dad decided to go so we all got cleaned up and went to town.

It was the largest crowd of people I had ever seen in Inez. I'm clueless about the numbers of people but there had to be thousands. The little one-way street in and out of town was crammed with people. We stood for what seemed like a couple of hours and finally some big helicopters started flying over town. The buzz was that President Johnson was arriving.

President Johnson, his wife Lady Bird, and Kentucky's Governor Edward T. Breathitt would board a black convertible Cadillac and slowly come through the streets of Inez. Sure enough, 30 minutes or so later here came President Johnson and a small motorcade. I stood on the street with some other elementary children with my mom and dad close by and waved until the motorcade passed.

Johnson returned the same way he came because there was only one route to get back to the helicopters. Before he came back President Johnson and the motorcade continued on down Route 3 past Fannin's grocery to the very far end of south Milo Road. They were paying a visit to the Tom Fletcher family.

The picture of the entourage visiting Fletcher and his family was posted in almost every newspaper in the United States. I've heard that President Johnson asked Fletcher if he had any good drinking water and that Fletcher gave the President a drink from some water he had in a bucket on his front porch.

This was Johnson's way of gaining national attention and support for his new war on poverty. We thought Johnson was just coming to see us but there was a political agenda. We knew some of the families in Martin County had a tough time but we didn't realize that we were living in poverty. Later, we started hearing reports on the television that President Johnson had been to visit the poorest county in the United States.

"Poorest County in the United States." We all questioned that statement from family to school to the local citizens. We didn't feel right about that analysis. Statistically, we were down on the economic bottom. We just didn't feel that way about our county. However, only a totally blind person would not be able to see that a lot of families were very poor and had a very tough time.

Johnson and his entourage with dozens of media followers took their now famous pictures at Fletcher's to depict the state of Appalachian poverty. Johnson told Fletcher he was going to help him. Then Johnson said goodbye and he and the motorcade drove back through Inez. We were still there waiting. We waved again. Norma Testerman had positioned herself in front of the courthouse. Johnson's car stopped in front of the courthouse. Johnson shook hands with Norma and a few other people. Norma was thrilled saying "He shook hands with me, asking me my name and where I was from."

Later the helicopters filled the sky briefly while President

Johnson and Lady Bird flew off. The rumor mill had it that Fletcher received money in the mail from all over the United States. However, as with all mountain stories only Fletcher and his family know the real story.

This was just the beginning for the whole country. Soon people throughout the county started receiving government checks. I never saw one but we heard amounts were anywhere from $200 to over $400 and they came every month. People started applying for and receiving something called food stamps. We were told that people were allocated over $100 a month. In 1964, $100 would still buy some groceries.

There is no doubt there were families in every county in Eastern Kentucky who struggled and surely tremendously appreciated the free checks. People were going to the store like they had never gone before. People had money like they had never had before. The money was free and from the government.

Over the weeks, months and years, people would drive by the little frame house were Tom Fletcher lived. People would say, "That's where the President visited." Actually, people still drive by there. When he was running for President of the United States in 2008, Senator John McCain came to Inez. Guess what he wanted to see? Someone had to drive him down Route 3 to see the house Lyndon Johnson had visited.

Last I heard some of the Fletcher family still lived there and that Tom passed away in 2004 at the age of 78. The house where Fletcher lived never changed and his economic situation didn't appear to change much either.

After Johnson's visit people got fatter in Martin County and eventually throughout the country. I guess the new welfare checks and food stamps were paying off, but paying off in the wrong way. If you have nothing you are grateful for anything. Unquestionably people had to be grateful. However, the day of being grateful soon passed to expectancy and entitlement.

Many families who learned the entitlement system stayed on the entitlement programs. Children in the sixties grew up on entitlement programs and became dependent on food stamps and any kind of government check they could qualify for. For a number of families in Martin County, throughout all of Appalachia and even now throughout the entire United States the entitlement programs have become a malignant epidemic that is killing our nation.

Lyndon Johnson talked about a great society. A great society is not a society that is crippled by welfare and a people dependent on the handouts of the government. Where does the government get the money to hand out to everybody? The government steals it from the people who work and gives it to the people who do not work. That is not a great society.

Any great society will help the helpless and those who cannot help themselves. People become aged, sick or disabled in life. A great society does not cast off her hurting people. The country and the people band together to protect their own. But with all of life there has to be balance.

In America we don't have 50 million people who deserve to be on food stamps and government assistance programs. We are now tipping the scales of imbalance. In our nation there are as many people on free handouts as there are people who are working. This is not a great society.

A great society was across the creek on Milo Road. My grandma and grandpa worked six days a week. Every morning at about 9:30 my dad would pull in the driveway. He had driven from Holden, West Virginia from his coal mining job. His face was black from the underground coal mine he had worked. Mom would have a hot breakfast prepared for him. He did a few chores around the house. We had a garden that Mom and Dad tended. We had livestock. Everybody was busy. There was plenty to do.

Dad would shower and go to bed. We all had to be quiet. He had to sleep because he would drive two hours early in the evening to work the third shift late at night in the mines. On Friday he brought a paycheck home. He always paid Grandpa Hinkle whatever we charged during the week at the store and he supported his wife and family of five kids during the week.

Later, he helped Geneva, Clyde and me go to college. None of the three of us received any federal money for college education. With our dad's help and each of us working we graduated from Kentucky colleges.

There were times when life was really lean. Once Dad fell off a barn, broke his back and was out of work for six months. When I went to see him he was writhing in the worst pain and crying. He was that way for days. I was 12 years old at the time. When Christmas came I knew not to expect anything. When you are 12 you can sense when Mom and Dad are scraping to survive.

My mother handed me a little box on Christmas Eve. I was truly stunned. It was the greatest Christmas gift I had ever received and I had not even opened the box. When I opened the box it was an Elgin watch. It had a green band and even cooler, when I was in the dark the numbers on the watch glowed! Wow, I was so thrilled!

In about six or seven months Dad went back to work. It was a long dry spell. Mom and I had been looking at the Sears Catalog the day before Dad got hurt. Mom was going to order me two or three new shirts. All buying got put on hold until after Dad's recovery.

Looking back, we had the great society modeled by a mother and a dad who worked every day. Mom worked every bit as hard as Dad and maybe a lot of days harder. She cooked, kept the house and washed clothes. She worked right beside Dad in the garden and with the livestock and raised five children. Oh, that's another thing. We had lousy water. It was terrible for washing clothes. We caught rainwater and if it had not rained in a week or so we would have to carry water from the creek. That was always a tedious job because if we stirred the water just a little it would get sandy and we couldn't use it. So we had to dip carefully and then it was a haul carrying that water back to the house.

We had our own well. This was long before the day of a city or county water system. The day would come when Dad would be able to add a water treatment softener to our system and that was a blessing. Today, people all over the continent of Africa still carry water for miles.

We had a great society modeled by grandparents who stayed together and worked as a team and raised 10 children. They paid their taxes, were moral, law-abiding people and their lives made an impact on all the family.

Mom and Dad would stay together 63 years. Dad worked 30 years in an underground coal mine. Mom worked about 10 years as a teacher's assistant in the county school system.

They were always extremely busy people. They farmed, mowed grass, kept the house very organized and clean and went to church. I didn't realize it as a child but we had a great society.

Chapter 22
Vietnam

I played with most of the boys who lived on Milo, which had been known as Stidham. There were lots of playmates. There was my first cousin Kevin, Buz, Slim Daddy, Garry and Larry from Tomahawk and there were numerous others. We would often spend an entire Saturday or Sunday roaming the hills or playing hide and seek. Sometimes we would spend afternoons playing music. I'm not sure my mom and dad thought it was music. Periodically, several of us camped out throughout the summer months. We would camp at Milo Lake, Dad's big log barn, or out in the middle of the hills.

Buz had an older brother named Roe who was commonly known as Junior. Junior was drafted out of high school, sent to boot camp, and eventually Vietnam. Junior came home in a casket. He was a sergeant for the Marines and died on June the first, 1970 at the age of 21 from a grenade explosion. I was about 15 years old at the time. Junior's untimely death in Vietnam and lying in state at their family's home was worse than a horror movie.

Junior rode the school bus home with us during a lot of his high school days so we talked to him every day. It was all very personal for everybody who lived on Milo and in the county.

Casualties such as Junior's and thousands more only escalated our family fears when Clyde was drafted into the Army six months after graduating from college. He was working and had only been married a short time.

Dad, Mom, Clyde and his first wife and I all rode to the Huntington, West Virginia airport the day he left for Vietnam. We stopped at Mama and Grandpa's store to fill up with gasoline. Mama and Grandpa walked out to the car to tell Clyde bye and Mama cried and waved as we drove away. Clyde went to Vietnam and every day we watched the evening news to hear about what was going on in that long drawn out war.

There was no email, social media or cell phones. We had to wait for a letter to arrive to find out any news. Mail from Vietnam came slowly but we were always very relieved when the mail arrived. Clyde returned home safely from Vietnam and his two-year draft into the Army was over. Uncle Haskel and Maude's son Eugene went to Vietnam three times.

The military funeral with a seven gun salute and the presentation of the flag to Junior's dad Mr. Hopson was gut wrenching. We gathered on the side of the hill at the Fannin Cemetery on Milo to watch this take place and to grieve with the family.

Recently, I went to Washington, D.C. and saw Roe Junior's name on the Vietnam memorial. It was a solemn moment. Looking back I believe I would have greatly enjoyed serving in the military. Unfortunately, the Vietnam War did not make military service very appealing.

Chapter 23
Something Strange on the Front Porch

In the summer I would often be at Grandma and Grandpa's store until the edge of dark. I would leave the store with just enough light to walk south on Milo toward our bridge. The bridge always made me nervous. I imagined there might be someone hiding underneath the bridge, possibly a troll or something. Whatever it might be I did not want him, her or it to have the opportunity to reach up and grab me. At night I would ease across the bridge and then by the time I got to the end of it I would break into an Olympic style 100-yard dash until I stepped onto our front porch.

One particular summer night I had just stepped onto the bridge from the highway when I heard noise on the front porch. This time I slowed down as I stepped on the bridge. It was just dark enough that it was unclear whether I was seeing Mom and Dad on the porch. As I neared the end of the bridge I became certain it was Mom and Dad. They were standing and embracing each other but it sounded like they were in distress. I feared something was wrong. I wondered if maybe they had been in a heated argument or just what was going on.

Reaching the end of the driveway I realized they were crying and holding onto each other. I walked up the concrete steps to the front porch and stepped around them and sat down for a moment on the porch. They were talking different. Dad acted like he was talking to somebody else but I looked around and didn't see anybody else. Mom was doing the same thing. Dad would periodically reach his hand upward like he was trying to touch the ceiling and Mom occasionally did the same thing. The conversation was passionate and mingled with tears.

I got up and went into the house because whatever they were doing was bewildering. About 30 minutes later it was over and Mom was back in one of our bedrooms sewing. I approached her quietly and asked "Mom what were you and Daddy doing out there?" Mom quietly responded with a little smile "Your daddy was saved tonight."

"Saved? What in the heck was my mother talking about? Saved from what?" I didn't really get it at that moment. I was six or seven years old and had never seen anything like that before.

The picture became increasingly clearer in the days ahead. The next Sunday morning we were at the Inez Freewill Baptist Church. There was an altar call and my dad along with others went to the front of the church and got down on their knees. They stayed there for a few minutes while several were kneeling there praying.

I understood they were praying because I had attended church at the Tomahawk Sulphur Springs Church a few times and had developed an understanding about postures people assumed when they appeared to be praying.

After their prayer time was finished we loaded up in our cars and drove down to the beginning of Route 3 and parked our cars in the vicinity of the county health department. We got out of the car and started walking down to the creek. This was really strange. When we got to the creek a couple of men who were preachers of the church were preparing the crowd of about 100 people who had gathered. One was talking about baptism and the other would eventually pray.

Three people entered into the water to be baptized. My dad and to my surprise my first cousin Vonda got into the creek along with another man that I did not know. In time I would later to come to know him as Clyde Waller who married my first cousin Josephine.

Each of the three would be baptized and several of us watched from the banks and the road as each one was immersed in the creek. There was a display of emotion and great feeling at this baptism as they came up out of the water. There were expressions of "Praise the Lord! Amen!" And, there were tears of rejoicing.

Dad's salvation would begin a whole new era in his life. One that was good. From this point forward it seemed that Mom and Dad were in church every weekend. Actually it was practically two or three times a week. They would go Sunday morning and Sunday night. Often they would go on a Friday or Saturday night and sometimes even one night during the week. It wasn't this way every week. Some weeks it did seem like a lot.

It wasn't long before Dad and Mom made a church membership decision and ended up at Sulphur Spring United Baptist Church. This would be their church throughout the rest of their lives. It had been Mama and Grandpa Hinkle's church when they were able to go.

Church gave Dad the opportunity to utilize his bass singing voice. He had a good bass voice and Mom had a nice tenor voice. They were soon singing in the choir. Choir music would eventually lead them into friendship with Clyde and Lula Mae Testerman. They formed a quartet and sang together for several years. They would sing at the different United Baptist Churches in the county and sometimes go to other counties to sing.

I spent many nights at the Testerman's house watching television with Norma and Leah Sue while our parents practiced singing for two or three hours in the back of the house. And then there were the many nights they practiced at our house on Milo.

I heard them practice so much that being confined with it in the house really got old. It was really difficult to watch television when the gospel quartet music practice was going on in our house. Looking back it was a wonderful time in many ways for Mom and Dad as they both loved to sing and most of the church people in the county loved to hear them.

One summer day I would answer the telephone. Clyde Testerman was on the phone. He wanted to talk to Dad. He told me Lula Mae had been killed on the Inez Road going to work. She was driving a Volkswagen and as she turned a sharp curve going down the hill a drunk driver was speeding on her side of the road and the head on collision ended her life.

I ran to the garden where Mom and Dad were hoeing corn. I told them that Clyde Testerman was on the phone and what he was saying. Dad rushed to talk to him and cried as Clyde told him about Lula Mae's sudden death.

The music changed after that for a long time. Mom, Dad and Clyde Testerman occasionally would try to sing but it was of course never the same. Mom and Dad would eventually sing with other people and continue their love of singing gospel music. A couple of years later Clyde remarried and his second wife also loved to sing and they even sang some with Mom and Dad but it wasn't with the every week fervency that it had been before

Lula Mae's death.

Chapter 24
Summer

Very rarely do I remember being bored. I always found a way to occupy my time. After Wanda, Geneva, Arvel and Clyde moved on there were times that I would be lonely. Our house had gone from a place of massive activity with five kids to one kid who was only eight years old when Clyde went on to college. I was only 12 by the time he was married and really gone.

Summers were long. School ended the last of May and then we were usually back in school by the middle of August or sometimes the last week of August. My summers were filled with playing basketball, the guitar and riding a Western Auto three speed yellow bicycle up and down Milo Road. I would often ride that bicycle four to six miles a day up and down Milo.

There were the times throughout the week when we hoed corn, sprinkled bean dust, hoed potatoes and pulled weeds in the garden. We also had about two acres of grass that had to be cut with a push lawn mower. From the time I was eight years old that project was mine to be done during the week. Sometimes my dad, mom and I would do it but Dad expected me to get it done during the week. This was an aerobic workout like no other. We didn't have powered weed eaters or other powered mowing devices.

There were numerous boys who lived up and down Milo and it seemed like we planned a camp out almost every week or two. Those were the days when children could still go out in the hills of Martin County and camp out.

Once Buz and I were riding our bikes over into Richardson. At the time Richardson was in the middle of nowhere. It got dark so we made a makeshift tent by throwing a tent over our two bicycles. We had blankets that we put on the ground. We got our flashlights out, ate our food and started sharing scary stories.

Scary stories always come to you when you are camping and all you can hear are owls and other critters making sounds in the night. We used to camp in my dad's barn back up in the holler behind our house. Sometimes it was loaded with hay and that's when it was really fun. We could really make a cave out of a massive number of bales of hay.

I fished and squirrel hunted until I was about 14 years old. My first cousin Kevin and I caught a lot of fish considering the number we had available in our creek. Once we were fishing up under Junior and Lucille's bridge and Kevin told me "Throw your line over there across the creek." Within seconds a 12-inch bass grabbed my line. It was one of the biggest fish I ever caught out of that hole of water. Kevin laughed "I didn't think there were any fish over there!"

The creeks were clean in Martin County in the sixties. You could stand on any bridge and count the fish in the water below. When you threw a fishing line in the water you could actually see what you where fishing for.

The county and a lot of Eastern Kentucky gave up their clear streams of water in the early seventies. The fish in our streams died and for years the water was always dark. Coal mines that formed in our county brought major dollars. People began building new houses, driving new cars and wearing nice clothes. The economy became robust. What we lost were the fish in our streams. The area's streams of water became polluted.

We had a difficult time drinking tap water from our own well as it was filled with sulphur. This was unrelated to coal mining as we had sulphur water before coal mining. The treatment devise that Dad had put on our well helped but it was never great water.

About 200 yards north of our house on Milo we had a nice swimming hole. There was a brush pile that had formed in the creek. It was actually causing some of my dad's cow pastureland to erode away making the creek a bit wider in that particular spot. It became a great place to swim. Two to three times a week several of us would gather at the brush pile for a summer swim. There was one spot that was actually about six feet deep, which was incredible for a small creek. We would dive some into that area and luckily none of us ever broke our necks.

The cow pasture was a great place for basketball games. Arvel and Clyde along with James and others on the creek had managed to erect a very nice wooden basketball backboard and goal in the cow pasture about 100 yards from the house. Dad always had a dozen cows or more and so every time we played basketball we had to clean the cow "stuff" off the basketball court. The cows seemed to enjoy utilizing the basketball court for their bathroom activities.

My older brothers and their friends played a lot of basketball on that court. I was little and usually watched from the sidelines or occasionally they would let me throw the ball inbounds. That court became a haven for me as a kid. I would play for hours in make-believe ball games with some of the greatest competition in the world. No one could ever stop me on that court.

The ball court would become a place my buddies and I would

eventually hang out and shoot basketball for several summers. If you are raised in Kentucky having access to a basketball goal is a necessity of life.

Chapter 25
Loving Music

Mom, Dad and the Testermans would sing for hours at least one night a week. In the summer they would sing on the front porch and everybody up and down the creek could hear them. They sang without any instruments or recorded music. Sometimes Dad would blow a note on a pitch pipe. They would hum a moment and then take off singing.

My brother got a new Kay Mandolin when I was in the second grade. In time I would play it occasionally when he wasn't around. When I was seven or eight James taught me to play a few chords on the mandolin and the guitar. Soon I would buy a bass from a guy named Lynn who also lived on Milo and loved listening to a band called Cream.

Kevin and I played a lot of music together. I learned very few songs but was always trying to write songs. I wrote bluegrass songs and some rock n' roll songs. I first started playing music with Garry and Larry Fitzpatrick when we were about eight years old. Their brother Paul played with Clyde, James, Don Fannin and Joe Copley. Garry, Larry and I got to play their half-time intermission a couple of times. Garry played the guitar and Larry the bass fiddle. It was fun.

One night at Grassy we were supposed to play a show and Garry and Larry's brother helped us. We entertained for about 30 minutes. I recall singing Barefoot Nellie and Good Ol' Mountain Dew. The crowd was congenial. We were unnerved by the time the show started. At least 10 guys banged on the door where we were practicing and harassed us to let them into the building so they wouldn't have to pay to watch the fall festival. We never let them in. The principal who had invited us was Floyd Horn. He had warned us "Don't let anybody in that door." We didn't but they screamed, and threatened us for an hour. For guys nine or ten years old it was unnerving.

Kevin and I began playing more music. We became captivated by the sounds of the sixties rock music. We played some with Jack Ward out behind the post office in Tomahawk. This lasted about a summer and then we played with Steve Endicott and then Gary Ward. We played a lot until I was about a junior in high school.

I spent most of my time writing songs. Most of the songs we performed were songs I had written. We played with some other guys in Martin County for awhile and then we left them. I was told that they took one of my songs and recorded it as a record.

Kevin, a guy named Slim Daddy and I were playing our electric guitars and drums on the front porch of our house one evening. We were loud. My mother came out and said, "If you all don't stop I'm going to go crazy." We stopped.

Chapter 26
Late Night Cramps

For several years my mother suffered from severe leg cramps. On a couple of occasions she had been in the Paintsville hospital for blood clots in her legs. Anytime from 11:00 at night until 3:00 in the morning they seemed to happen. I would hear my mother in pain, unable to stand up and holding on to the cramp in her leg. Often Dad would be working at night.

I would jump out of my bed and go to the drawer in the kitchen where we kept a rubber hot water bottle and then begin running hot water from the tap. The whole time I would hear my mother writhing in pain. Finally I would fill the rubber bottle and take it along with a towel for her to place against the cramp. Usually in 10 or 15 minutes the cramp would subside. On occasions we would have to boil water on the stove. The tap water would not always be hot enough to stop the cramp. I could never handle my mother or father being in pain.

Mom worked all the time. A better word might be toiled. On Mondays she had a long day of washing clothes for seven people. We had a ringer washing machine until I was seven or eight years old. The clothes would eventually dry on the outdoor clothesline. She would then be ironing late Tuesday and probably into Wednesday. However after Mom and Dad installed an automatic washer and dryer my mother continued to work hard. She always found something to do. The house was always clean. She made sure we kept the yard looking good, flowers planted and always food to eat. She worked in the garden with Dad and during times when we were financially lean we had food to eat. Between my father working sometimes six days a week, having a garden and Grandpa's grocery store across the road, we did alright.

After Dad fell off the barn there could have been some weeks that Grandpa carried us with groceries. However, I don't know this to be so. If Grandpa did I do know Mom and Dad were sticklers about paying off any grocery bills or any other kind of debt. The only debt I remember us having for a long time was a regular car payment. Even car payments stopped as we kept a '67 Chevy Caprice for a long time.

Mom entertained and cooked for a lot of people. It was common for Dad's brothers to visit from West Virginia. Elbert, Opal, Russell and Lou often came together and would spend the night. Russell had a bit of humor and imagination and would play with me as a child. I always had some kind of a game that Russell and I could play. He usually played along for a while.

Soon my mother would cook for grandchildren. We often had Wanda and Glen and their children. Normally this meant later in the day Geneva and Harold and their children would be over for a larger get together. Arvel visited two or three times a year with his family. Clyde lived in Columbus for a while and would often come with his wife and children. In time, Wanda and Clyde and their families moved back and built homes on the family property. All of these people came and visited in our home and Mother was always cooking and cleaning for family. It was a wonderful time in the lives of our family. The routines of getting together, visiting, sharing food around the table and laughing are fond memories. We always had a lot to talk about and something to laugh about.

I can remember my mother shouting once in church. She was sitting right behind me and it scared me to death. Shouting in church was common at Sulphur Spring Baptist Church. As a child I often thought it was entertaining to watch people clapping their hands, shouting "Praise the Lord" and sometimes jumping all over church. My mother never did that but one time she did feel a unique visit from God and she cut loose with a big burst of "Praise the Lord" and hand clapping. On another occasion she had been in bed for a couple of weeks. Dad, the Testermans and maybe a couple of other people came to sing and they had a little church service going and Mother began to shout "Praise the Lord" while she was in bed.

Mom was an amazing woman. She sewed beautiful quilts. Worked hard all week and took care of everybody. On Sunday she dressed up and went to church. When Dad became a Christian they both dressed up and went to church. I heard a preacher say a long time ago that one of the ways to keep a marriage together is for the couple to put on the best clothes they have and go to church every Sunday. Mom and Dad did that a minimum of once a week and sometimes more. They stayed together 63 years. Maybe there is something to the preacher's philosophy.

Mom worked as a teacher's aid for the county board of education for about 10 years. I think it was something different to do other than working at home all the time. She took a number of extension classes earlier on in hopes of earning a college degree but she was never able to complete her degree. She was smart and in my earlier years helped me do a lot of homework.

Mom was a great person. She was loyal, worked hard, loved to sing and loved her family. After leaving home I would call her once or twice a week and usually talk a half an hour.

Chapter 27
Wrecking the Truck

I always loved for Mom and Dad to go to church because I could watch television as loud as I wanted, play Beatles music or crank up my electric guitar. Kevin was over one night and we were doing really well playing our guitars and singing songs. Suddenly a light bulb went off in my mind and I got this really bright idea. "Kevin let's take Dad's truck for a drive." Without missing a beat he responded "Okay." We climbed in Dad's old truck and took off down our driveway, across the bridge and up north Milo Road. I was 15 and did not have a driver's license. I had barely driven the truck in the driveway and never on the highway before.

We sailed along and decided to turn onto the road that led to a community called Richardson. The road was still gravel and visibility on this road was not great. Yet, we were having a great time. We talked, listened to the radio and were enjoying being out in Dad's truck.

A moment later I misjudged the road and was driving over a 20' culvert into a large ravine. Neither of us was wearing a seat belt but somehow we escaped without much injury. We looked at each other in terror and started climbing out of the truck. I only had one thing on my mind and that was getting the truck out of the ravine and back home before Dad and Mom got back from church.

Richardson was remote. There were no cell phones in that day and few landline telephones. As we climbed up the bank we heard lots of noise and suddenly there were about 200 plus people looking down at us. A little church less than 50 yards from our wreck was startled by all the noise we had created. They were in the midst of a big revival service and had a large gathering. They rushed down to the scene to see if we were okay.

I was frantically asking about someplace where I could make a telephone call for a wrecker to pull the truck out. Someone pointed me in the direction of a house and said, "That family down there has a telephone." We walked down the pitch-black road and knocked on the door.

"Sir, I've wrecked my truck. May I please use your telephone?" The man and wife were very gracious. They gave me the number for a man with a wrecker and the call was probably long distance. Almost all calls were long distance in that day. I thanked them and left to wait on the wrecker.

Kevin called his dad and by the time we got back to the scene of the accident Kevin's father had arrived. The wrecker showed up and pulled the truck out of the brush. I was of course penniless but gave the wrecker man as much information as I could and promised him we would pay him.

Miraculously, the truck was not damaged too bad and could be driven. As I started home Kevin jumped into the truck with his dad. I would make the very long drive home knowing that it was past time for Mom and Dad to be home from church and that I would have to face the music.

As I drove across our bridge I could see my dad standing in the doorway of our front porch. Most of the downstairs lights in the house were on as well as the porch light. As I drove up the driveway I knew this would be my last night of life on earth.

I drove the truck to the back of the house, which is where my dad commonly parked it. Getting out of the truck I rushed to the smokehouse bedroom behind the house and locked the door. Sitting on the side of the bed I soon heard my dad's voice. "Glenn, are you alright?" "Yes, I am okay." "Well, get out of there and get in the house."

I did not want to open the door to that smokehouse. I knew I would be confronted by my dad's face and that he would likely kill me or at least shake me or beat me. I had no choice so I slowly opened the door and there he stood. I walked down the step of the smokehouse and headed through the backdoor of the house knowing he would grab me at any moment. My mother was in the house but at this point was not saying a word. As I walked into the house I made a beeline for the upstairs and headed to the back room. I was terrified of what was going to happen but I couldn't get away from Dad. He came upstairs to get out of his church clothes and sternly said, "I will never let you get a driver's license" and walked back down the steps.

It was a long night but I lived. Dad never touched me. Nobody beat me. The only thing I could figure out was that maybe church was working. He had been to church and probably had a great time. Most likely he had been up front singing. I knew at that moment that there surely must be a God.

I would go on to get a driver's license soon after I turned 16. I even worked one summer and made $400 to buy an old Chevy Chevelle from Dick Ward at the Chevy dealership. I would later wreck that car and end up in the hospital for two weeks. The first person who was at my side in the emergency room was my dad. As I was lying there with a mangled leg and blood covering my face I said, "Dad I'm so sorry for all this." With nothing but love coming from the part of his very soft heart, in which I believe God had done His work, he said, "Honey, it's alright."

I only saw that part of my dad at such moments. Years later when we lost a little stillborn baby my daddy pulled me into the spare room of our house and we cried. At this time in my life I didn't need a penny from anyone but he insisted on giving me $400 to help with the burial costs. This was a side of him that came out during the worst of times.

Trust me, he could still be very difficult at times but in the worst moments and when I seemed to be on the brink of destruction, he and Mom always loved me.

Chapter 28
Bible School

Summer baseball dominated our schedules for a couple of years. Sterling Ward was kind enough to turn the field behind his house into a baseball diamond. A bunch of us played baseball on that field a day or two a week.

One summer I either struck out or pop flied out every time I went to bat. I don't recall having one base hit. I knew how bad I was when Marvin, our catcher, starting putting his catcher's equipment on whenever I went to bat and there were two outs. I got better the next summer and hit several homeruns and always had a couple base hits per game. There is something about hanging in there, practicing and not giving up.

One day while we were practicing baseball Teresa Ward invited me to Bible school. The Bible school was only a short three-mile bicycle ride to Tomahawk and so I agreed to attend. I rode my bicycle Monday through Friday every morning and participated in the two-hour or so session of Bible study, recreation, crafts and refreshments. Several of my other friends were there and so it was fun.

On the last day of Bible school Linda Hinkle presented a lesson about eternal life and the importance of having Christ in our hearts and being prepared for eternity. The last thing I wanted to do was go to hell after death. The teacher led us in a prayer we could recite if we wanted to invite Jesus Christ into our hearts. I prayed that prayer to invite Jesus into my life. Two of my close classmates, Jack and Polly Ward were sitting beside me and they likewise prayed the prayer to receive Jesus.

I was excited but nervous about all of this. All I knew about church and religion was what I had experienced in the local churches and there wasn't anything about it that I liked. I actually thought church was boring and would rather do anything other than go to church.

I didn't realize at that moment I had really made a life-changing decision. I couldn't accept that becoming a Christian was as simple as believing in Christ. I wanted to believe, did believe and accepted Him but it seemed too easy. Linda talked on the phone with me on two or three occasions and read over and over the scriptures that refer to "believing" on Christ. I wrestled the entire weekend about this decision. I told my mother about the decision at Bible school and she had a bit of uncertainty about my decision as well. Within the weekend I reconciled that I wanted to follow Christ and live for Him. I was 15. A 15-year-old can make a decision but firm decisions are not without a price.

Chapter 29
Biking to Church

On the next Sunday morning I got up and put on the best clothes I owned. I remember putting on a yellow shirt, black bell bottomed dress pants, orange socks and two-toned dress shoes. I got on my bicycle and headed for Inez. That July 17th was scorching hot. However, I was skinny and could run for miles. After riding over two hills I arrived in Inez with a bit of a sweat. I parked my bicycle in Russell Williamson's yard and walked into church. For years Russell Williamson was the principal of Inez High School. I would later be ordained with Mr. Williamson.

Jimmy Grayson, the pastor of First Baptist Church, greeted me and said he was excited to hear about my decision. He preached a good sermon and then gave what is commonly known as a public invitation to follow Christ. I along with several others responded that Sunday morning by walking down the aisle of the church, shaking the preacher's hand. We were later introduced to the church as new followers of Christ.

The whole thing was emotional for me. All of this was a big deal. This was something I had planned to do when I was 99 years old and one day before I died. I had never dreamed of making such a decision at the age of 15.

I rode my bicycle back to Milo from Inez and told Mom and Dad about my decision. Later that afternoon Mama Hinkle was visiting our house. She looked up at me with her sweet smile and affirmed what I was doing by saying "I am so glad you are making the right decision." Later that evening Mom, Dad and I went back to Inez in the family car. Several of us including Jack and Polly were baptized that evening by pastor Jimmy Grayson.

Chapter 30
Grandpa and Mama's Funerals

Grandpa died in the Louisa hospital on May 28, 1969. A couple of years before, I thought Grandpa was going to die in the dining room of his house. Mom, several of her siblings and I were visiting with Grandpa and Mama when suddenly Grandpa started looking very uncomfortable. He reached into his pocket and pulled out a tiny pill and put it under his tongue. He began to complain of chest pains and his breathing was a little heavier. Everyone in the room became anxious and it got quieter as Grandpa was very uncomfortable.

Soon he was putting another tiny nitroglycerin pill under his tongue and he looked to be on the verge of breaking a sweat. But then the discomfort he was feeling passed. He sat back into his chair, became more comfortable and said, "I'll probably never live to see another Christmas." He actually did make another Christmas but the time came when he made that fateful trip with James to the hospital.

Grandpa would die during his two-week stay in the hospital. One day I sat by the fire in Grandpa's old store and James reflected that maybe if Mama had been with him in the hospital he might have lived longer. She would often get up in the middle of the night to pound his back and get his heart back in rhythm. The nurses probably just weren't close by when this happened to him in the hospital.

Grandpa would lie in state in his casket in the living room of his house for two evenings. It seemed like everyone sat up with Grandpa for two nights. Mama's house beside the Hinkle grocery store was a place of constant activity. There was a lot of food on the big kitchen table. People came and went. Grandpa was lying in state in the living room of the house. The casket lid was open for all to see Grandpa's body.

The funeral would be on the front porch of the house. It was a Sunday afternoon. The weather was nice. All nine children, James, grandchildren and great grandchildren would be at the funeral. We would sit in the yard, around the sides of the house, around the gasoline pumps and stand along the edge of the highway. A lot of people were at Grandpa's funeral.

I had walked out into the backyard to cry. I couldn't believe we had lost Grandpa. Harold came out into the backyard and in his own way tried to comfort and get me through the moment. I was not prepared for the emotion that my mother, Kathleen and Eva Nell expressed when they went up to the casket for the last goodbye. My mother touched the body of Grandpa and wept out loud in distress. After an outpouring of grief they would soon walk away from the casket.

Grandpa would be loaded into the hearse and taken to the Hinkle cemetery just about 200 yards from their prior home place and where his previous country store began. Numerous family members are buried there today. Mama would come home to an empty house and a store business to run. She would not be totally alone. James and his wife had made a place to live over the store where Grandma and Grandpa used to sleep. Numerous children were close. Haskell, Junior, Sebern, Mom, Lorenz and Kathleen were not far away. Plus there were several grandchildren. Mama would have the love and support of family.

However, Mama was 78 years old and her own mortality was facing her. She would try to shoulder the store business for a few months but she started looking tired and sometimes I thought she looked distant. I'm sure she was thinking about Grandpa and missing him. The two of them together even at 78 and 83 years of age were maintaining the store, and maintaining life. There was more competition in the grocery and gasoline business. Age had slowed them down. They were not prospering by any means but they were amazing for a senior couple.

Within two weeks of becoming a Christian I felt an internal call to be a minister. By March of 1971 I would preach my first sermon to a full house at First Baptist Church Inez at the age of 16. I preached on the Second Coming of Christ. On Sunday evening I preached a message on Jonah and eight school age friends and kids came forward during the invitation to accept and follow Christ. My mama was not able to come to the services but while I was visiting with her the day before she said "I prayed all my life for one of my sons to be a preacher. God has answered that prayer through you."

Mama would get weaker. She looked lonelier and no longer stood erect. The broad smile that I had seen so many times was rarely seen. She eventually had to close the store since she did not have the physical stamina or health to keep it going.

The store closed. The soda pop, ice cream, candy, and grocery items that lined the shelves disappeared and soon the doors were locked and Grandpa and Mama Hinkle's store became history. We would never again experience sweet summer days and a point of community and family fellowship.

Mama would die on June 3, 1971 in the old Paintsville hospital where I was born. I would later spend two weeks in the same room where she died because of my car accident. In so many ways, her funeral was very much like Grandpa's funeral. The house became a place of massive activity. There was lots of food on the table in the dining room. My mother and a number of the family sat up with Mama for a couple of nights. She was lying in state in the living room and then on Sunday afternoon there was the same very large number of people who attended her funeral as had attended Grandpa's funeral. My mother and her sisters stood before the casket and profusely wept with outbursts of grief. She was taken and buried beside Grandpa at the Hinkle cemetery just past the house were Haskell and Maude lived.

The store was closed. Grandpa and Mama had gone to be with the Lord. Life had changed for all of us on Milo and our family. We only had two choices to make. We could move forward or live in the past. We all moved forward but even today I find myself thinking back to how it all used to be at Grandpa and Mama's store.

CPSIA information can be obtained
at www.ICGtesting.com
Printed in the USA
BVHW072135150122
626250BV00001B/60

9 780990 925088